RUSSIAN FOLK TALES

Translated and retold by

H.C. STEVENS

Illustrated by

ALEXANDER LINDBERG

Paul Hamlyn · London

Published by
Paul Hamlyn Ltd
Drury House · Russell Street · London WC2
for Golden Pleasure Books Ltd
© Copyright 1967 by Golden Pleasure Books Ltd
Printed in Czechoslovakia

Contents

8   Prince Ivan and the Grey Wolf

16   The Apples of Youth and the
Water of Life

30   The Frog Princess

38   The Dun Horse

44   Maria Morievna

56   The Swan-Geese

60   'Go to "I do not know where" and
bring me "I do not know what" '

78   Finist, the White Falcon

96   Beautiful Vassilisa

106   The Golden Fish

110   Marko the Wealthy and Vassily
the Luckless

120   As the Pike Orders

128   The Magic Ring

Prince Ivan
and the Grey Wolf

ONCE UPON A TIME there was a tsar named Berendey, who had three sons. The tsar's palace was surrounded by a beautiful orchard, and among the trees in the orchard was a wonderful apple-tree which bore golden apples. One day the tsar discovered that someone was getting into the orchard and stealing his golden apples. He was furious, and sent his guards to catch the thief. But though they watched all night they were quite unsuccessful.

The tsar was so upset at the loss of his golden apples that he lost his appetite too. His sons tried to comfort him, and the eldest told him:

'I will go and guard the orchard against the thief tonight, father.'

And he went off to the orchard. But although he arrived there quite early in the evening and walked about for some time, he saw no one. So he lay down on a grassy bank and soon fell asleep.

Next morning his father asked him:

'Well, have you good news for me? Did you see the thief?'

'No, father,' his son answered. 'I did not sleep a wink all night, I did not even close my eyes. But I saw no one.'

The following night the tsar's second son went to guard the orchard. But he, too, slept all night, and next morning he told his father he, too, had seen no sign of a thief, although he had not closed his eyes.

Now it was the turn of the youngest brother, Prince Ivan, to guard the orchard. And he was so anxious not to miss the thief that he was afraid even to sit down, let alone to lie down. When he felt he was getting drowsy he washed his face with dew, and this made him wide-awake again. About halfway through the night he thought he saw a light in the orchard. It grew brighter and brighter, until all the trees were lit up. Then he saw that the

light was coming from a Firebird, which was sitting on the apple-tree and pecking at the golden apples.

So he crept up very quietly to the tree and caught hold of the bird by the tail. But the Firebird spread its wings and flew away, leaving only one tail feather in Prince Ivan's hand.

Next morning, when he went to report to his father, the tsar asked him:

'Well, Ivan, did you see the thief?'

'Dear father,' Ivan answered, 'I cannot say I caught him, but I have found out who is eating our apples. And I have brought you a tail feather in proof. It is the Firebird.'

The tsar took the feather and looked at it, and no longer felt sorrowful; but he thought a great deal about the Firebird, and one day he sent for his sons and told them:

'My dear children, I want you to saddle good horses and ride forth into the world to see whether you can find and bring back the Firebird.'

The young men bowed to their father, saddled good horses, and set out on their travels: the eldest in one direction, the second son in another, and Prince Ivan in a third direction.

Ivan rode along for many hours; but, as it was a fine summer's day, he began to feel tired. So he slipped off his horse, hobbled it, and lay down to sleep. When he woke up some time later, he saw that his horse had gone. He set out to look for it, and finally found it. But now it was only a heap of gnawed bones.

The prince was in despair, for how could he travel about the world without a horse?

9

He still had to go on looking for the Firebird, so he set off on foot. He walked on and on, and grew terribly tired. He sat down on some soft grass and gave way to his gloomy thoughts. Suddenly a grey wolf ran up to him. It asked him:

'Why are you looking so miserable, Prince Ivan?'

'I have good reason to feel miserable, grey wolf,' the prince answered. 'I have lost my good horse.'

'I ate your horse, prince, for I was hungry. But I do feel sorry for you. Tell me why you have travelled so far, and where you are going.'

'My father has sent me to ride through the world until I find the Firebird.'

'Why, you could have ridden even on your good horse for three years and never found the Firebird for only I know where it lives. I ate your horse, so now I will serve you faithfully and well. Get on my back and hold on tight.'

Prince Ivan seated himself astride the grey wolf, and it loped away, past the green forests, and the azure lakes. At last they came to a very high fortress. There the grey wolf told Ivan:

'Listen to me, and remember what I say. Climb over the wall and do not be afraid; all the guards are asleep. In the attic you will see a small window; in the window hangs a golden cage, and in that cage is the Firebird. Take the bird and hide it under your coat; but be sure not to touch the cage.'

Prince Ivan climbed over the wall and saw the attic. And, just as the wolf had said, in the attic window a golden cage was hanging, and the Firebird was in the cage. He took out the bird and put it under his coat. But as he looked at the golden cage he could not help coveting it. It was made of precious gold; how could he leave it behind? He completely forgot what the wolf had told him. But as soon as he touched the cage the alarm was sounded all through the fortress; drums rolled and trumpets blared, the guards woke up, captured Prince Ivan and took him to Tsar Afron.

The tsar was furious at this attempt to steal the Firebird and the cage, and asked the prince:

'Who are you, and where are you from?'

'I am Prince Ivan, the son of Tsar Berendey,' Ivan replied.

'How shameful! The son of a tsar coming here to steal!' the tsar exclaimed.

'That is as may be,' the prince retorted. 'But your bird flew to our orchard and stole the golden apples.'

'In that case you should have come to me and asked me for the Firebird and I would have given it to you out of respect for your father. But now I shall see to it that all the world knows of your behaviour! And in order to earn my forgiveness you will have to enter my service. A certain Tsar Kusman has a horse with a golden mane. Bring that horse to me, and I will give you the Firebird and the cage.'

Prince Ivan was downcast at the thought

of having to undertake such a task, and he went to tell the grey wolf what had happened. But the wolf said to him:

'I told you not to touch the cage. Why did you disobey me?'

'I know I did wrong; but forgive me, grey wolf.'

'It is easy enough to ask forgiveness,' the wolf answered. 'All right, get on my back again. We will not turn back now.'

Once more the grey wolf loped off with Prince Ivan on its back. And at last they came to the fortress where the horse with the golden mane was stabled. Then the wolf told Ivan:

'Climb over the wall; do not be afraid, the guards are asleep. Go to the stable and bring out the horse. But be sure not to touch the bridle you will see hanging there.'

The prince climbed over the wall into the fortress, and saw that the guards were asleep. He went straight to the stable and found the horse with the golden mane. But his eyes fell on a bridle hanging up; it was of gold and studded with precious stones: the only bridle fit for a horse with a golden mane. And he put out his hand to take it. But at once the alarm was sounded all through the fortress; drums rolled and trumpets blared, the guards woke up, took the prince a prisoner and led him before Tsar Kusman.

'Who are you, and where are you from?' the tsar asked Ivan.

'I am Prince Ivan.'

'To attempt to steal a horse shows little wisdom! Even a peasant would not try to do that. But I will let you off, Prince Ivan, if you agree to enter my service. A certain tsar named Dalmat has a daughter, the beautiful Helen. Carry her off and bring her to me, and then I will give you the golden-maned horse and the golden bridle.'

At this verdict Prince Ivan was even more downcast than before. Again he went to see the grey wolf. But the wolf said:

'I told you not to touch the bridle. You did not obey my orders.'

'Nevertheless, forgive me, forgive me, grey wolf,' the prince pleaded.

'It is all very well, saying "forgive". All right, get on my back.'

Once more the grey wolf raced off with Prince Ivan on his back, until they came to Tsar Dalmat's fortress. But this time the grey wolf said to the prince:

'I am not going to send you this time, I am going myself. You set off on the road back to Tsar Afron; I will soon catch up.'

Prince Ivan obediently started to go back, while the grey wolf sprang over the fortress wall and into the garden. In the garden the beautiful Helen was walking with her attendants. The wolf sat behind a bush and watched them, and the moment the princess fell a little way behind her attendants the wolf seized her, flung her over his back, and scampered away.

Ivan had gone some distance when the grey wolf caught up with him, bringing the beautiful Helen sitting on its back. The prince was delighted, but the wolf said:

'Quick, get on my back, in case we are followed.'

The prince sat on the wolf's back behind the princess, and the wolf rushed away with them, past the green forests and the azure rivers and lakes. At last they arrived at Tsar Kusman's fortress. But the prince seemed very sad, so the wolf asked:

'Why are you silent, Prince Ivan? Are you sad?'

'Have I not good reason to be, grey wolf? How can I part with this beautiful princess? How can I exchange her for a horse?'

'I will see to it that you are not parted from her,' the wolf promised. 'We will hide her somewhere, then I will turn myself into the beautiful Princess Helen, and you can lead me to the tsar.'

So they hid the princess in a forest hut. Then the grey wolf uttered a magic spell and at once became her living image. Prince

Ivan took her to Tsar Kusman. The tsar was delighted and said:

'Thank you, Prince Ivan, for getting me such a beautiful woman for my wife. Take the golden-maned horse and the bridle.'

The prince bridled the horse, mounted it, and rode off to the hut where the true Helen was hidden. He seated her behind him on the horse, and they rode away.

Meanwhile, Tsar Kusman made arrangements for his wedding, feasted all day and half the night, and, when it was time for bed, he led the mock-princess into his bedroom. But when he lay down beside her on the bed he found he was lying not with a beautiful young wife, but with a grey wolf. He was terrified and fled, and the wolf slipped away and out of the fortress.

When the wolf caught up with Prince Ivan it noticed that he was looking sad again, so it asked:

'Why are you so thoughtful, prince?'

'I have good reason to be. I am sad to think I have to give up the golden-maned horse in exchange for the Firebird.'

'Do not be downhearted; I will help you,' said the wolf. When they arrived at Tsar Afron's fortress the wolf said:

'You go and hide the horse and the princess. Then I will turn myself into the golden-maned horse and you can take me to Tsar Afron.'

So they hid Helen and the horse in the forest. The grey wolf uttered a magic spell and became a golden-maned horse, and Ivan led the horse to the tsar. Tsar Afron was delighted, and gave him the Firebird and the golden cage as well. The prince carried the cage with the bird into the forest, seated the princess on the golden-maned horse, and rode off on his journey back to his native country.

Meanwhile, Tsar Kusman gave the order for the golden-maned horse to be brought to him. But when he tried to mount it the horse turned into a grey wolf. The tsar was so frightened that he fell to the ground, while the grey wolf made good its escape and soon overtook Prince Ivan.

'Now I must say goodbye; I cannot come any farther,' it told the prince.

So Ivan dismounted from his horse and bowed very low three times, thanking the grey wolf respectfully. But the wolf said:

'Do not bid goodbye for ever to me. I shall yet be of service to you.'

'How can you be of any further service to me?' Ivan thought. 'All my wishes have come true.' He mounted the golden-maned horse and rode away with beautiful Helen and the Firebird. He arrived in his own country, but as he still had some way to go to reach home he decided to have a rest at midday. So they ate some food, drank water from a spring, and lay down to rest.

No sooner had the prince fallen asleep than his brothers happened to ride past, and saw him. They had travelled far and wide in search of the Firebird, but of course they had not found it. When they saw their

brother lying asleep and noticed that he had the Firebird, the horse with its bridle, and even a beautiful girl, they plotted to kill their brother and take everything for themselves.

So they killed Prince Ivan, seated themselves on the golden-maned horse, put beautiful Helen on another, and threatened her:

'You must not say a word to anyone when we get home.'

Then they rode off, with the horse, the princess, and the Firebird, to their father.

They left Prince Ivan lying dead, with the crows already gathering above him. But suddenly the grey wolf ran up and caught one crow with its young chick.

'Crow, you must fly away and bring back to me some sparkling water and some still water,' the wolf told the crow. 'If you bring back the two sorts of water I will let your young one go.'

The crow agreed, and flew off, while the wolf watched over the chick. In due time the crow flew back with both the sparkling and the still water. Then the wolf sprinkled Ivan's wounds with the still water, and the wounds healed; it sprinkled him with the sparkling water, and the prince revived.

'I have had such a deep sleep,' he yawned.

'Yes, you were sleeping very soundly,' the grey wolf said. 'But for me you would never have awakened. Your own brothers killed you and carried off all you had gained. Now get on my back, quick!'

The wolf raced off in pursuit of the two elder brothers, and soon caught up with them. It tore them to pieces and scattered them over the field.

Prince Ivan bowed and thanked the grey wolf once more, and said goodbye to it for ever. He mounted the golden-maned horse, and rode home with the princess. He had obtained the Firebird for his father, and beautiful Helen as a wife for himself.

Tsar Berendey was delighted to see him with the Firebird, and asked him to tell of all his adventures. Prince Ivan told his father how the grey wolf had helped him to win the Firebird, the horse, and the beautiful Helen, how his brothers had killed him while he was asleep, and how the wolf had restored him to life and then torn them to pieces.

The tsar mourned the loss of his two sons, but he was soon comforted, by the wedding of Prince Ivan and the beautiful Princess Helen, and they lived happily ever after.

The Apples of Youth
and the Water of Life

ONCE UPON A TIME, in a certain kingdom a tsar had three sons: the eldest was named Fiodor, the second Vassily, and the youngest Ivan. The tsar grew old and his sight very poor, and he heard that beyond twenty-seven lands, in the thirtieth kingdom was an orchard. In the orchard a tree was growing which bore apples that could restore youth, and under the tree was a well of living water. If an old man were to eat one of these apples he would grow young again, and if a blind man were to wash his eyes with this water, he would have his sight restored.

So the tsar made a great feast, summoned all his princes and noblemen and said to them:

'Which one of you brave lads will volunteer to ride beyond twenty-seven lands into the thirtieth kingdom, and bring me back some apples of youth and water of life? I would give half my kingdom to such a hero.'

But when they heard what the tsar desired, the tall men began to hide behind those of average height, and those of average height behind the short ones. But not one of them, whether tall or short, offered to go.

So then Prince Fiodor stepped forward and said:

'My father, we do not wish to see half the kingdom handed over to anyone. I shall ride to the thirtieth kingdom and bring you back the apples of youth and a pitcher of the water of life.'

He went to the stable, chose an unbroken horse, bridled it with an unused bridle, took a whip that had never been cracked, and fastened his saddle on the horse with twelve saddlegirths, for strength. Then he set out on his journey. Everybody saw him mount his horse, but no one saw the direction he took.

He rode all day until nightfall, until the crimson sun was setting. Then he came to a crossroads, where he had a choice of three roads. At the junction a flat stone was lying on the ground; on it was written:

'If you ride to the right, you save yourself but lose your horse. If you ride to the left, you save your horse but lose yourself. If you ride straight ahead, it is into the marriage bed.'

The prince thought it over, and decided to ride straight ahead, into the marriage bed.

16

So he took that road. He rode and rode until he came to a tower with a golden roof. A beautiful girl ran out of the tower to meet him, and said:

'Son of the tsar, come, share my hospitality and rest and sleep for the night.'

'No, my girl,' he replied. 'I do not want your hospitality, and if I sleep it will not shorten my road. I must ride on.'

'Son of the tsar, do not be in such a hurry to ride on, but come with me. It will be good and pleasant for you.'

Without waiting for his consent the girl pulled him out of the saddle and led him into the tower. She gave him food and drink and put him to bed. But the moment he lay down on the wall side she overturned the bed, and he dropped into a deep cellar.

Some time later the tsar again gave a banquet; he summoned his princes and noblemen and said to them:

'Now, my brave lads, who will volunteer to go and bring me some apples of youth and a pitcher of the water of life? I will give half my kingdom to that hero.'

Once more the tall noblemen began to hide behind those of average height, and these in turn hid behind the short ones. But not one of them volunteered.

So his second son, Prince Vassily, stepped forward and said:

'Father, I do not want to see the kingdom handed over to a stranger. I shall ride and bring you back what you ask.'

He went to the stables, chose a horse that had never been ridden before, bridled it with an unused bridle, took a whip that had never been cracked, and saddled the horse with twelve saddlegirths. Then he rode away. Everybody saw him mount his horse, but no one saw the direction he took. He rode till he came to the crossroads where the flat stone was lying, and read the inscription:

'If you ride to the right, you save yourself but lose your horse. If you ride to the left, you save your horse but lose yourself. If you ride straight ahead, it is into the marriage bed.'

The prince thought and thought and then rode straight ahead, to where he was to be married. He rode up to the tower with the golden roof, and a beautiful girl ran out to meet him. She asked him to accept her hospitality and to come in and rest.

'Son of the tsar,' she said, 'do not be in any hurry to ride on, but come with me and you will find it good and pleasant.'

Without waiting for his agreement she

17

pulled him out of the saddle, led him into the tower, gave him food and drink and put him to bed. But as soon as he lay down on the wall side she again overturned the bed, and he fell down into the cellar.

Down in the darkness someone asked him:

'Who is that?'

'It is Prince Vassily. But who is already down here?'

'Prince Fiodor.'

'Well, brother, so now we are both caught.'

After a time the tsar again gave a banquet, he summoned all his princes and noblemen, and asked them:

'Who will volunteer to bring me some apples of youth and a pitcher of the water of life? I will hand over half my kingdom to such a horseman.'

But once more the tall nobles hid behind those of medium height, and those of medium height behind the short ones. And again no one volunteered. So Prince Ivan stepped forward and said:

'Give me your blessing, father, for I will ride to the thirtieth kingdom, to bring back the apples of youth and the water of life. And I shall search for my brothers at the same time.'

The tsar gave him his blessing, and the prince went to the stables to choose a horse to his mind. But the moment he looked at any horse it shivered, and when he put his hand on any horse it fell over. He could not find any horse that pleased him, and he went away very downcast. In the yard he fell in with some old kitchen woman, who said to him:

'Greetings, Prince Ivan. Why are you looking so miserable?'

'I have got good reason to, Old Woman,' he answered. 'I cannot find a horse to my liking.'

'You should have asked me first. In the cellar you will find a horse standing tethered by an iron chain. If you can take that horse, you will find it suits you.'

The prince went to the cellar, pulled back its iron cover, and jumped down to the horse. It reared up to him and set its forelegs on his shoulders. He stood without moving. Then the horse pulled away the iron chain from the wall, jumped out of the cellar and dragged Ivan out after it. The prince bridled it with an unused bridle, saddled it with a new saddle, and fastened the saddle with twelve saddlegirths, for youthful glory.

Then he set out on his journey. People saw him mount his horse, but no one saw the direction he took. He rode as far as the crossroads, but there he sat thinking.

'If you ride to the right, you lose your horse. And how far can I get without a horse?' he thought. 'If you ride straight ahead, it is into the marriage bed. But that is not why I have set out on this journey. Ride to the left, you save your horse. And that is the best road for me.'

So he turned down the road where he would save his horse but would himself be lost. He rode all day through the green meadows, over the stony mountains, till nightfall. The crimson sun was setting when

18

he came to a little hut. The hut was standing on a chicken leg, and had one small window. The prince called out in a loud voice:

'Little hut, little hut, turn your back to the forest, your front to me. As I enter you, so may I come out again.'

The little hut turned its back to the forest, its front to Prince Ivan. But first he went into the forest, where he saw a very old witch, Baba Yaga. She was spinning and combing a hank of silk.

'My goodness!' she said when she saw him. 'Who has ever heard or seen a Russian before! But today a Russian has himself arrived.'

The prince said to her:

'Ah, you bony-legged old witch, you are plucking your bird before you have caught it, you are running a young man down before you know him. You would do better

to jump up at once and give this traveller food and drink and a bed for the night. Then I would lie down, you would sit at the head of the bed and question me, and I would tell you whose son I am and where I come from.'

So the old witch did as he had asked: she gave him food and drink and put him to bed. Then she sat by the bed and questioned him:

'Whose son are you, my good young man, and where are you from? What country do you come from? Whose son are you?'

'I, Old Woman, am Prince Ivan, the son of the tsar of such and such a kingdom. I am journeying beyond twenty-seven lands to the thirtieth kingdom, to obtain the water of life and apples of youth for my father.'

'Well, my dear child, you have a long way to go. The water of life and the apples of youth are to be found growing only in the country ruled by the great heroine, the Maiden Blue-Eyes. She is a kinswoman of mine. I do not know whether you will get what you want . . .'

'Grannie, you add your wise head to my powerful shoulders. Give me your good advice.'

'Many young men have ridden past this hut, but not many spoke politely to me. Take my horse, child. It will be better than yours. It will carry you to my middle sister, and she will tell you what to do.'

Next morning Prince Ivan got up very early, and washed himself very thoroughly. He thanked the old witch for his night's lodging, and rode off on her horse.

Suddenly he said to the horse:

'Stop! I have dropped my glove.'

But the horse answered:

'I have galloped two hundred miles since you started to speak.'

So he rode on again. The day drew on towards nightfall. Ahead of him he saw a little hut standing on a chicken leg; it had one small window. He said to the hut:

'Little hut, little hut, turn your back to the forest, your front to me. As I enter you, so may I come out again.'

The little hut turned with its back to the forest, its front to the prince. Suddenly he heard a horse whinny, and the horse he was riding whinnied in answer. For the two horses had the same mother.

The old witch Baba Yaga—she was even older than her sister—heard the prince's horse whinny, and she thought:

'My sister has come to pay me a visit.'

And she opened the front door. But when she saw the prince she exclaimed:

'My goodness! Who has ever heard or seen a Russian before? But now a Russian himself has arrived.'

'You bony-legged old crone,' the prince said to her, 'address a man according to his clothes, but always treat him with respect. You should stable my horse, and give me, a fine young man and a traveller, food and drink and a bed to sleep in.'

The old crone did as he wished; she stabled the horse, gave him food and drink, and put him to bed. Then she asked who he was, where he had come from and where he was going.

'I am Prince Ivan, son of the tsar and I am riding to the land of the mighty heroine, the Maiden Blue-Eyes, to get the water of life and apples of youth for my father.'

'Well, my son, I do not know whether any good will come of it for you. It is difficult to get to Princess Blue-Eyes.'

'Grannie, you add your wise head to my powerful shoulders. Advise me what to do.'

'Many young men have ridden past here, but not many have spoken politely to me. Take my horse, child, and ride to my older sister. She will tell you better than I what to do.'

So Prince Ivan spent the night in the old witch's hut. Next morning he got up very early and washed very thoroughly. He thanked the old woman for the night's lodging and rode off on her horse. And this horse was even swifter than its brother.

Suddenly the prince said:

'Stop! I have dropped my glove.'

But the horse answered:

'I have galloped three hundred miles since you started speaking.'

A story is soon told, but a journey takes longer. Prince Ivan rode all day until nightfall, when the crimson sun was setting. Then he came to a little hut standing on a chicken leg; it had one small window. He called to the hut:

'Little hut, little hut, turn your back to the forest, your front to me. I am not staying for ever, only for one night.'

The hut turned its back to the forest, its front to Ivan. Suddenly a horse whinnied, and the horse under the prince whinnied back. An old witch, Baba Yaga, came to the door; she was even older than her sisters.

She looked and saw that the horse was her sister's, but its rider was a stranger, a handsome young man. Prince Ivan bowed to her respectfully and asked for a night's lodging. He apologised for asking, but travellers did not carry their lodging about with them. Everyone needed lodging, whether he came on horse or foot, whether he was rich or poor.

The old witch did as he requested: she stabled the horse, and gave the prince food and drink. Then she asked him who he was and where he was going.

'I, Grannie, am Prince Ivan, son of the tsar of such and such a kingdom. I called on your youngest sister, but she sent me to her middle sister, and your middle sister sent me to you. Add your wise head to my powerful shoulders, advise me how I can obtain water of life and apples of youth from Princess Blue-Eyes.'

'So be it: I will help you, Prince Ivan. The Maiden Blue-Eyes, my kinswoman, is a strong and mighty heroine. All round her kingdom is a wall twenty-one feet high and seven feet wide. At the gate is a guard of thirty heroines. They would never let you in through the gate, so you must arrive at the dead of night, riding my fine horse. When you come to the wall, whip the horse on its flanks with a whip never used before. Then it will jump over the wall. Tether it and go into the orchard. There you will see an apple-tree with the apples of youth growing on it, and under the tree is a well. Pick three apples, but do not take more. And draw a pitcher of the water of life from the well. The Maiden Blue-Eyes will be asleep. Do not go into her room, but get on the horse and whip its flanks. It will carry you back over the wall.'

Prince Ivan did not stay the night with this old woman, but seated himself on her fine horse and rode off through the night. The horse galloped along, leaping over the mossy marshes, past the rivers and lakes.

In the dead of night the prince rode up to a very high wall. At the gate the guards, thirty mighty heroines, were asleep. He urged on his good horse, lashed it with an unused whip. The horse was maddened, and it flew over the wall. He jumped to the ground, entered the orchard, and saw an apple-tree bearing silver leaves and golden apples; under it was a well. He picked three apples, and drew a pitcher of water from the well. Then he felt a great longing to see the mighty and powerful heroine, the Maiden Blue-Eyes, herself.

So he went into her bedroom. There he found six powerful maiden heroines sleeping on one side, and six on the other, and the Maiden Blue-Eyes lying in the middle. Even in her sleep she was an Amazon.

The prince was mastered by an irresistible impulse to kiss her. He did so without awakening her, then he got up, and went out. He mounted his horse. But it spoke to him in a human voice:

'You disobeyed us, Prince Ivan. You went into the chamber of the Maiden Blue-Eyes. And now I shall not be able to jump over the wall.'

But he lashed the horse with his unused whip, and shouted:

'Why, you bag of grass, you dinner for wolves, we cannot spend the night here, we would lose our heads.'

The horse was even more furious than before, and it leaped over the wall. But one of its shoes struck against it and set strings sounding; bells started to ring. The Maiden Blue-Eyes woke up and realised that someone had taken her apples. She called:

'Get up! We have been robbed.'

Then she ordered her horse to be saddled and galloped with twelve brave maidens in pursuit of Prince Ivan. He drove his horse on as fast as it could gallop, but Princess Blue-Eyes began to catch up with him. When he rode up to the hut of the oldest witch she already had a horse waiting for him. He leaped from one horse to the other and fled further. The prince flew out of one gate, the Princess Blue-Eyes in at the other. She asked the old witch:

'Grannie, have you seen an animal roving this way?'

'No my child,' the witch answered.

'Grannie, have you seen a young man riding this way?'

'No, child. But you have had a long ride, so let me give you a drink of milk.'

'I would like a drink, but it would take some time to milk the cow.'

'Why should it, child? I will be quick.'

So the old witch went to milk the cow, but she milked it slowly. When Princess Blue-Eyes had drunk her milk she set off again after Prince Ivan.

Meanwhile, he rode up to the second sister, changed horses, and tore off. As he went out through one door, Blue-Eyes came in at the other.

'Grannie,' she asked, 'have you seen an animal roving this way, or a fine young man riding past your little hut?'

'No, my child. But you have had a long ride, so stop and have some pancakes.'

'But it will take so long to cook them.'

'Why should it, child? I will be quick.'

The old witch made and cooked pancakes, but she made them slowly. Princess Blue-Eyes ate some, then she set out again after the prince.

He rode up to the youngest witch, slipped off his horse, mounted his own splendid horse and tore away. As he went out through one gate the Maiden Blue-Eyes rode in at the other. She asked the old witch whether a handsome young man had ridden that way.

'No, my child,' the witch answered. 'But you have had a long ride, so stop and have a bath before you continue your journey.'

'But it will take you a long time to heat the water.'

'Why should it, child? I will be quick.'

The old witch heated the bath and made everything ready. The Maiden Blue-Eyes steamed herself, then splashed herself with cold water, and set off again in pursuit. Her horse leaped from hill to hill, dashed past rivers and lakes. And she began to overtake Prince Ivan.

He saw behind him twelve heroic maidens, led by a thirteenth, Princess Blue-Eyes, ready to ride him down, to strike his head from his shoulders. He reined in his horse; Blue-Eyes galloped up and shouted to him:

'You thief, why did you drink from my well without asking permission? And you

did not even put the well cover back afterwards. And why did you steal my apples?'

But he said to her:

'Yes, I took them. But now let each of us ride back three leaps of our horses, and then we will try our strength.'

So the prince and the maiden took three leaps of their horses away from each other, and armed themselves with clubs, lances, and sharp sabres. Then they rode at each other three times; they smashed their clubs, they broke their lances and ruined their sabres, but neither could unhorse the other. There was no point in their charging again on their horses, so they sprang to the ground and engaged in hand to hand fight. They fought from morning till evening, until the crimson sun was setting.

Then Prince Ivan's nimble foot twisted under him, and he fell to the damp ground. The Maiden Blue-Eyes set her knee on his chest and drew her dagger to plunge into his breast. But he said to her:

'Do not kill me, Maiden Blue-Eyes; it would be much better to take me by the hand, raise me from the earth, and kiss me on my lips.'

And so she did; she raised Prince Ivan from the damp ground and kissed him on his lips. They pitched a tent in the open field, in a spacious meadow. There they plighted their troth and exchanged rings.

At the end of the third day the Maiden Blue-Eyes said to the prince:

'I shall ride back now to my own country. But you go home; be sure not to turn aside anywhere. In three years' time you can expect me in your kingdom.'

The maiden and the prince mounted their horses and rode off in opposite directions. When he came to the crossroads where the flat stone was lying, he thought:

'This is a fine thing! Here am I riding home, but my brothers are lost without trace.'

And he did not obey the command of Princess Blue-Eyes, but turned down the road which led to the marriage bed. He came to the tower capped with a golden roof. As he rode up his horse whinnied, and his brothers' horses answered. For they were all from the one mother.

He went to the door and knocked with his ring; the top of the tower shook, the window-sills were twisted. A beautiful girl ran out.

'Ah, so it is you, Prince Ivan. I have been waiting for you a long time. Come and share my hospitality and spend the night in sleep and rest.'

She led him into the tower and gave him refreshment. But he dropped under the table more than he ate or drank. Then the girl led him into the bed chamber, saying:

'Lie down, Prince Ivan, and sleep and rest.'

But the prince pushed her on to the bed, smartly turned it over, and she flew down into the cellar. He bent over the hole, and called:

'Is anyone alive down there?'

The answer came:

'Prince Fiodor and Prince Vassily.'

He drew his brothers out of the hole; they were filthy and unkempt. He washed them with some of the water of life, and soon they were looking like princes again. Then they mounted their horses and rode away. When they came to the crossroads, Prince Ivan said to his brothers:

'Watch over my horse while I lie down and rest.'

He lay down on the soft grass and fell asleep, the sleep of a hero.

But then Fiodor said to Vassily:

'We are returning without the water of life or the apples of youth. No honour will be done to us, our father will set us to mind the geese.'

'We will throw Ivan over a precipice,' Vassily answered. 'And give the apples and water to our father.'

So they threw their brother over a precipice and took the apples and the water. Prince Ivan went falling into the abyss for three days and three nights. He fell right to the seashore, and when he came to himself he could see only sky and water. Some young chicks were squawking under an old oak by the shore, for the foul weather was plaguing them. So he took off his coat and covered the chicks, while he took shelter under the oak.

When the weather turned fine again a great bird called Nagai flew down, settled under the oak, and asked the chicks:

'My dear children, how is it the foul weather did not kill you?'

'Mother,' they answered, 'we were saved by a man who covered us with his coat.'

The bird asked Prince Ivan:

'How did you get here, my good man?'

'My own brothers threw me over the precipice in order to get hold of the apples of youth and the water of life.'

'Well, as you saved my children, ask whatever you wish, whether gold, silver, or precious stones.'

'I do not need anything, Nagai: neither gold, nor silver, nor precious stones. But would it be possible to take me back to my own country?'

'Get me two barrels, each containing four hundred pounds of meat,' the bird answered.

So on the seashore the prince shot geese and swans, packed them in two barrels, fastened under Nagai's right wing, and the other under her left wing. Then he perched himself on her back. As she rose and flew up into the sky he began to feed her from the barrels. All the time she was flying he fed her. But the distance was so great that he used up both the barrels. And she began to turn back. So he drew his knife, cut a piece of meat out of his own leg and gave it to the bird. Then she flew on and on. But once more she had to turn back. So he cut a piece off his other leg and gave it to her. Now she had only a short distance to fly. But she had to turn back a third time. So he cut a piece off his own breast and gave it to her.

And then Nagai carried the prince all the way to his own country. When they arrived, she said:

'You fed me well all the way, but in all

my life I have never tasted a sweeter piece of meat than the last.'

The prince showed her his wounds. The bird brought up the three pieces, telling him:

'Put them back in their place.'

He put them back, and the meat grew to the bone.

'Now slip down off my back, Prince Ivan,' the bird said, 'and I will fly home.'

He got down, and Nagai sailed up into the sky, while he went on his way through his native country.

When he arrived at the city he learned that Prince Fiodor and Prince Vassily had given their father the apples of youth and the water of life, and the tsar had been restored to health. He had become as healthy and strong as of old, and his sight was as keen.

Ivan did not go to see his parents but gathered around him drunkards and riff-raff from the taverns and went wandering from tavern to tavern.

Just about that time, in the thirtieth kingdom, beyond twenty-seven lands, the powerful heroine Blue-Eyes gave birth to two sons. And the children grew not day by day, but hour by hour. After three years had passed Blue-Eyes took her sons, assembled her soldiers, and went to look for Prince Ivan. She arrived in his father's kingdom, and pitched a tent of white linen in a green meadow. She lined the path from the tent with coloured cloths. And she sent a messenger to the tsar's palace to tell him:

'Tsar, hand over the prince. If you do not, I will put all your kingdom to fire and flood, and take you prisoner.'

The tsar was greatly alarmed, and sent his eldest son, Prince Fiodor, to her. The prince walked over the coloured cloths up to the tent of white linen. Two lads ran out, and asked:

'Mother, Mother, is that our father coming?'

'No, children. He is your uncle.'

'Then what do you order us to do with him?'

'Children, treat him hospitably.'

So the two boys picked up canes and set to work to flog Prince Fiodor. They beat and beat him until his legs could hardly bear him away.

But Blue-Eyes sent a second message to the tsar:

'Hand over the prince . . .'

The tsar was even more frightened, and

sent his second son, Prince Vassily. He went up to the tent. The two lads ran out, and asked:

'Mother dear, is that our father coming?'

'No, children, he is your uncle. Treat him hospitably.'

So the two boys beat and beat their uncle with canes, until his legs could barely carry him away.

Then Blue-Eyes sent a third message to the tsar:

'Go and find your third son, Prince Ivan. If you do not find him I will put all your kingdom to fire and flood.'

The tsar was terrified; he sent for Prince Fiodor and Prince Vassily and ordered them to find their brother. The two brothers fell at their father's feet and confessed how they had taken the apples of youth and the water of life from Ivan while he was asleep, and had flung him over the precipice.

When the tsar heard their story he wept bitterly. But meanwhile Prince Ivan himself was already on his way to Princess Blue-Eyes, taking the riff-raff from the taverns with him. As they went up to the tent they tore the cloths with their feet and threw the pieces all over the place.

As the prince approached the tent of white linen, two lads ran out, asking:

'Mother dear, Mother dear, some drunkard is coming with a crowd from the taverns.'

But Blue-Eyes said to them:

'Take him by the hand and lead him into the tent. He is your own dear father. He has suffered innocently for three years.'

So they took Prince Ivan by the hand and led him into the tent. Princess Blue-Eyes washed him and combed his hair, changed his clothes, and put him to bed. She took the tavern riff-raff a glass of wine for each of them, and they drank her health and went home

Next day Blue-Eyes and Prince Ivan rode up to the palace. And the tsar gave a magnificent banquet, after which the prince and princess were married. But there was little honour shown to Prince Fiodor and Prince Vassily: they were driven out of the palace. The first night they slept wherever they could find a spot, the second night they did the same, but the third night nobody would take them in.

Prince Ivan did not remain in his father's kingdom, but rode off with Blue-Eyes to her own country.

The Frog Princess

and shot their arrows. The eldest son's arrow fell into a nobleman's courtyard, where it was picked up by his daughter. The second son's arrow fell into a merchant's courtyard, and it was picked up by his daughter. But the arrow shot by the youngest son, Prince Ivan, rose so high and flew so far that he didn't know where to look for it. So he started to walk, and at last he came to a marsh. In the marsh he saw a frog with his arrow in its mouth. He said to the frog:

'Frog, give me back my arrow.'

But the frog replied:

'Then take me for your wife.'

'Oh, come now,' the prince said, 'how can I have a frog as my wife?'

'But you must, for it is the tsar's will.'

MANY YEARS AGO a tsar had three sons. When they came of age he sent for them and said:

'My sons, before I am too old I want you to marry, and I would like to see my grandchildren.'

The sons replied:

'In that case, father, give us your blessing. But whom are we to marry?'

'My sons,' the tsar said, 'take your bows, go out into the open field, and shoot an arrow. Wherever it falls, there you will find your wife.'

The sons bowed to their father, took their bows, went into the fields, drew them

At first the prince tried to avoid it, but eventually he had to accept his fate and carry the frog home. Then the tsar arranged for the three marriages; his eldest son to the nobleman's daughter, his second to the merchant's daughter, and the unhappy Prince Ivan to the frog.

After the weddings the tsar summoned his sons again, and told them:

'I want to see which of your wives is the finest needlewoman. Each one is to make me a shirt by tomorrow.'

The sons bowed to their father and went to tell their wives. But when Prince Ivan arrived home he sat down looking very miserable. The frog was jumping around on the floor, and it asked him:

'You look very unhappy, Prince Ivan? Are you in trouble?'

'My father has ordered you to make him a shirt by tomorrow,' the prince answered.

'Do not worry, Prince Ivan,' the frog said. 'You just go to bed. You will feel better after a good sleep.'

So he went to bed. But the frog jumped out on to the verandah, threw off its skin and turned into the wise Princess Vassilisa, a maiden so beautiful that words could never describe her. She clapped her hands and cried:

'My faithful attendants, gather round and listen to me. Sew for me by tomorrow morning a shirt like the one my own father used to wear.'

When the prince woke up next morning the frog was jumping about the floor again, but a shirt wrapped in linen was already lying on the table. He was overjoyed. He picked up the shirt and took it to his father. When he arrived, the tsar was receiving the gifts from his two elder sons. The eldest son spread out the shirt his wife had made. As the tsar accepted it he said:

'This is a shirt for everyday wear.'

When the second son spread out his shirt, the tsar said:

'I could only go to the bath in that.'

Then Prince Ivan unfolded his shirt; it was embroidered with gold and silver threads in intricate patterns. The tsar took one look at it and declared:

'Now that *is* a shirt; I can wear it on important occasions.'

The two elder brothers went off home, remarking to each other as they went:

'It seems we were too quick to laugh at Ivan's wife; she is no frog, she is a witch.'

Now the tsar sent for his sons again, and told them:

'Each of your wives is to bake a loaf of bread for me by tomorrow. I wish to find out which is the best cook.'

When Prince Ivan arrived home after seeing his father he looked so miserable that the frog asked him:

'What is the matter, Prince Ivan?'

'You have to bake a loaf of bread for the tsar by tomorrow,' Ivan answered.

'Do not worry; just go to bed. You will feel better after a good sleep.'

At first the elder sons' wives had made fun of Prince Ivan's frog wife. But now they had changed their minds, and they sent an old kitchen woman to spy out how the frog was going to bake bread. But the frog, being wise, realised their scheme. After kneading the dough it made a hole in the top of the brick oven and poured the dough through the hole. The woman saw what had been done, and ran to the elder brothers' wives and told them. So they set to work and did the same.

But after Prince Ivan had gone to bed the frog jumped out on to the verandah, turned into the wise Princess Vassilisa, and clapped her hands:

'My faithful attendants, gather round and listen to me. Bake for me by the morning soft white bread like the bread I ate at my father's table.'

When the prince woke up next morning

the loaf of bread was already lying on the table. It was decorated with various fancy designs, and on its top was the shape of a city with walls and gates. He was delighted, wrapped the bread in clean linen, and took it to his father. When he arrived the tsar was receiving the loaves brought by his two elder sons. But their wives had poured the dough into the ovens just as the old woman had told them, and all they had to show for their labour were two burnt cinders. The tsar took the burnt loaf offered by his eldest son, looked at it, and sent it straight to the servants' quarters.

Then he took the loaf from his second son, and sent it after the other. But when Prince Ivan handed him his loaf the tsar said:

'Now this is such good bread, it should be eaten only on great occasions.'

The tsar had arranged a banquet for the following day, and he ordered his sons to attend with their wives. The thought of his frog wife attending a banquet made Prince Ivan feel far from cheerful, and he returned home with his head hanging. As usual, the frog was jumping about the floor. When it saw him it asked:

'Prince Ivan, what are you looking so miserable for? Has your father said something unpleasant to you?'

'How can I help looking miserable, frog? My father has ordered me to bring you to a banquet; and how can I show you to people?'

But the frog answered:

'Do not grieve, Prince Ivan. You go off to the banquet by yourself, and I will

follow later. When you hear a knock and a clap of thunder, do not be afraid. If anyone asks you what it means, just say: "That is my little frog who is coming riding in a little box."'

So he went off to the banquet alone. His elder brothers arrived with their wives dressed in their finery, wearing their jewellery, their faces painted and powdered. They laughed at Prince Ivan and asked:

'Why did you not bring your wife with you? You could have carried her in a handkerchief. Wherever did you find such a beauty? You must have searched all through the marshes for her.'

The tsar, his sons, their wives, and all the guests sat down at the oaken tables, which were spread with embroidered tablecloths. But before they started to feast there was a loud knock and a clap of thunder, so powerful that the palace shook. The guests were alarmed, and jumped up from their seats. But Prince Ivan said:

'Do not be afraid. It is only my little frog coming. She is riding in a little box.'

At that moment a gilded carriage drawn by six white horses drew up at the tsar's front door, and the wise Princess Vassilisa stepped out. She was wearing an azure gown studded with stars; on her head was a shining chaplet; she was so beautiful that

the guests sat and stared. She took Prince Ivan by the hand and he led her to the oaken table.

The guests began to eat and drink, and to make merry. But the wise Vassilisa only took one sip from her glass, pouring the rest into her left sleeve. She only nibbled at her plate of swan meat, and dropped the bones into her right sleeve. And when the two elder brothers' wives noticed what she was doing they followed her example.

After the eating and drinking it was time for dancing. The wise Vassilisa took Prince Ivan's hand and they danced together. And she danced so marvellously, so beautifully, that all the guests were amazed. Then she waved her left sleeve, and suddenly a lake was formed in the hall; she waved her right sleeve, and white swans floated on the lake. The tsar and his guests were filled with astonishment.

Then the elder brothers' wives also danced. And when they danced they waved one sleeve, but they only sprinkled the guests with wine; they waved the other sleeve, but only bones flew out. One bone hit the tsar in the eye, and he was so angry that he drove both the wives out of the palace.

Meanwhile, Prince Ivan quietly slipped out of the hall, and hurried home. He found the frog skin lying on the verandah and threw it into the stove, where it burnt in the fire. When Princess Vassilisa returned home she saw that the frog skin was gone. She sat down on a bench and said to her husband sorrowfully:

'Ah, Prince Ivan, what have you done? If you had waited only another three days I would have been yours for ever. But now I must say goodbye. You can look for me in the thirtieth kingdom beyond three times nine lands. There you will find me with Kashchey the Deathless.'

Then she turned into a grey cuckoo and flew out of the window. And the prince wept bitterly. Bowing to all the four points of the compass he went off into the world to seek his wife, the wise Princess Vassilisa. He walked for so long that he wore out his boots, his clothes were torn, and the rain soaked through his cap. One day he happened to meet a very old man, who asked him:

'Hello, young man! What are you seeking, where are you going?'

The prince told him how he had lost his wife, and was now seeking her. And the old man said:

'Ah, Prince Ivan, what made you burn the frog skin? You did not have to wear it or take it off. The wise Vassilisa was born cleverer and wiser than her father, and he was so annoyed that he ordered her to be a frog for three years. What is done cannot be undone. Take this ball; wherever it rolls, you follow boldly after it.'

The prince thanked the old man and started to follow the ball. It rolled along, and he walked behind it. In the open country he came across a bear, and took aim, intending to kill it. But the bear spoke to him in a human voice:

'Do not kill me, Prince Ivan. Some day I shall be of service to you.'

The prince had pity on the bear, and went on his way without shooting it. As he walked he saw a drake flying above him.

He took aim to shoot it, but the drake spoke to him in a human voice:

'Do not kill me, Prince Ivan. I shall be of service to you.'

So he had pity on the drake and went his way. Next a hare came running past. Ivan thought he would shoot the hare; but it said in a human voice:

'Do not kill me, Prince Ivan. I shall be of service to you.'

So he let the hare go, and went his way. He came to the blue sea and saw a pike lying on the sand of the shore. It was hardly able to breathe, and it said to him:

'Prince Ivan, have pity on me; throw me back into the blue sea.'

So he threw the pike into the sea, and followed the ball as it rolled along the shore. At last the ball rolled into a forest. There the prince saw a little hut standing on a chicken leg, and twisting round and round. He said to the hut:

'Little hut, little hut, stand just as you

were built, with your back to the forest, your front to me.'

Then the little hut turned with its front towards him, and its back to the forest. He went inside, and saw an old witch, the Baba Yaga, lying on top of the stove, her chin resting on the shelf at the top of the stove, and her nose pressed up against the ceiling.

'Why have you called on me, young fellow?' the old witch asked him. 'Are you seeking your fortune, or are you running away from it?'

'You old scold,' the prince answered, 'before you start asking questions you should give me food and drink and a hot bath.'

So the old witch Baba Yaga gave him a hot bath, gave him food and drink, and put him to bed. Then the prince told her he was seeking his wife, the wise Princess Vassilisa.

'I know, I know,' the old witch said.

'Your wife is with Kashchey the Deathless now. It will be difficult to get her away from him, Kashchey is not easy to deal with. His death is right at the point of a needle, the needle is in an egg, the egg is in a duck, the duck is in a hare, the hare is sitting in a stone chest, the stone chest is in the crown of a lofty oak, and Kashchey the Deathless guards that oak as he would the apple of his eye.'

Prince Ivan spent the night in the old witch's hut, and next morning she told him how to get to the spot where the lofty oak was growing. The prince found the spot, and saw the oak standing, rustling its leaves; in its crown was a stone chest, so high that it was very difficult to get at.

Suddenly a bear ran up and tore the oak up by its roots. The chest fell, and was smashed to pieces. A hare leapt out of the chest, and fled at top speed. But a second hare chased after it, overtook it, and tore it to pieces. But a duck flew out of the pieces, and sailed right up to the sky. However, as the prince watched, a drake flew at the duck; as he struck her she let fall an egg, and the egg dropped into the azure sea.

At the sight Prince Ivan shed bitter tears: how could he ever find that egg in the sea? But suddenly a pike swam up to the shore with the egg in its mouth. The prince broke the egg, took out the needle, and set to work to snap its point. As he snapped it Kashchey the Deathless struggled and writhed. But he could do nothing: the prince snapped off the point of the needle, and Kashchey died.

Then the prince went to Kashchey's white stone palace. The wise Princess Vassilisa ran out to meet him, and kissed him on his lips. So Prince Ivan and Princess Vassilisa returned home, and they lived happily to a ripe old age.

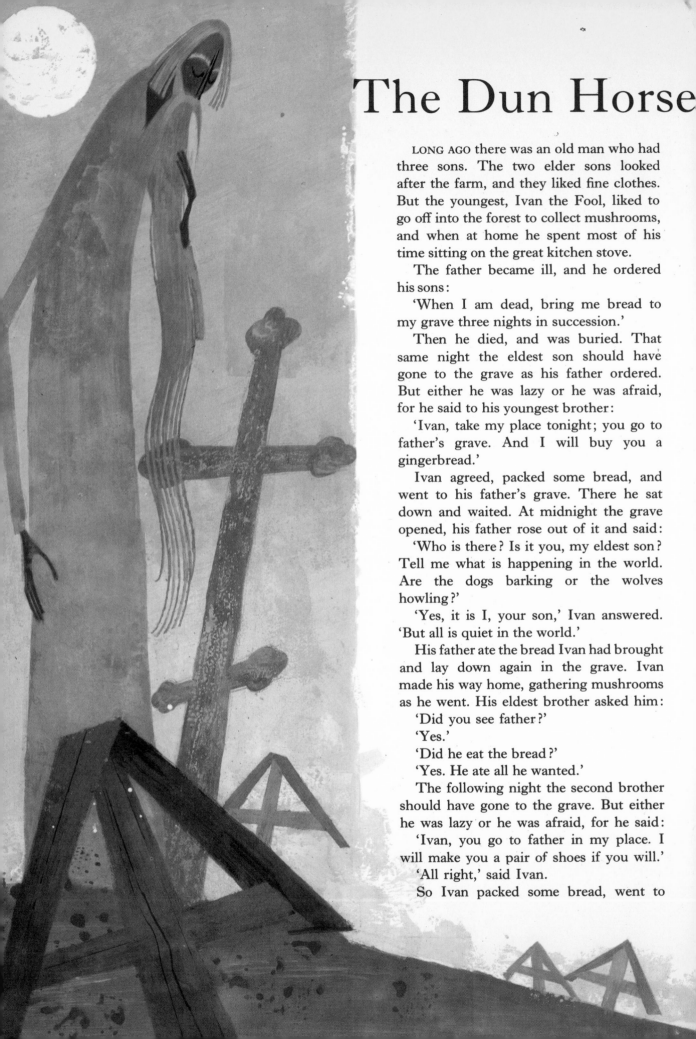

The Dun Horse

LONG AGO there was an old man who had three sons. The two elder sons looked after the farm, and they liked fine clothes. But the youngest, Ivan the Fool, liked to go off into the forest to collect mushrooms, and when at home he spent most of his time sitting on the great kitchen stove.

The father became ill, and he ordered his sons:

'When I am dead, bring me bread to my grave three nights in succession.'

Then he died, and was buried. That same night the eldest son should have gone to the grave as his father ordered. But either he was lazy or he was afraid, for he said to his youngest brother:

'Ivan, take my place tonight; you go to father's grave. And I will buy you a gingerbread.'

Ivan agreed, packed some bread, and went to his father's grave. There he sat down and waited. At midnight the grave opened, his father rose out of it and said:

'Who is there? Is it you, my eldest son? Tell me what is happening in the world. Are the dogs barking or the wolves howling?'

'Yes, it is I, your son,' Ivan answered. 'But all is quiet in the world.'

His father ate the bread Ivan had brought and lay down again in the grave. Ivan made his way home, gathering mushrooms as he went. His eldest brother asked him:

'Did you see father?'

'Yes.'

'Did he eat the bread?'

'Yes. He ate all he wanted.'

The following night the second brother should have gone to the grave. But either he was lazy or he was afraid, for he said:

'Ivan, you go to father in my place. I will make you a pair of shoes if you will.'

'All right,' said Ivan.

So Ivan packed some bread, went to

his father's grave, and sat down and waited. At midnight the grave opened, his father rose from it, and asked:

'Who is there? Is it you, my second son? Tell me what is happening in the world. Are the dogs barking or the wolves howling?'

'Yes, it is I, your son,' Ivan answered. 'But all is quiet in the world.'

His father ate as much of the bread as he wanted and lay down again in the grave. Then Ivan went home, gathering mushrooms on the way. When he reached home

his second brother asked him:

'Did father eat the bread?'

'Yes, he ate all he wanted.'

The next night it was Ivan's turn to go to the grave. But he said to his brothers:

'I have been the last two nights. Now one of you go, while I rest.'

But his brothers answered:

'Why, Ivan, you know the spot now; it would be better for you to go.'

'Oh, all right,' said Ivan.

He packed some bread, and went. At midnight the grave opened, and his father rose from it.

'Who is there?' he asked. 'Is it you, my youngest son? Tell me what is happening in the world. Are the dogs barking, or the wolves howling?'

'Yes, it is Ivan. But all is quiet in the world,' his youngest son told him.

The father ate the bread, and then said:

'You are the only son who has done as I asked. You were not afraid to come to me in my grave three nights running. Now go out into the open field and call: "Dun horse, magic horse, come when I call you." A horse will come galloping up to you.

39

Crawl into its right ear and out of its left, and you will be turned into a handsome young man. Mount the horse and ride it.'

Ivan thanked his father and went home, gathering mushrooms as he went. When he arrived home his brothers asked him:

'Did you see father?'

'Yes.'

'Did he eat the bread?'

'He ate all he could, and did not order us to go any more.'

But Ivan said nothing about the horse.

Just about that time the tsar issued a proclamation: all the fine young men who were not married were to assemble in the tsar's courtyard. His daughter, a girl of matchless beauty, had ordered a tower twelve logs high, and raised on twelve pillars, to be built for herself. She was going to sit at a small window in the top of the tower, and wait there until a young man riding a horse jumped right up to her and kissed her on the lips as he passed. Then, no matter what his birth or origin, the tsar would marry his beautiful daughter to this horseman, and would give half his kingdom as dowry.

Ivan's brothers heard of the tsar's proclamation, and said to each other:

'Let us go and try our luck.'

So they gave their horses a good feed of oats, dressed themselves in their finest clothes, and combed their hair. Ivan, who was sitting on the stove, said to them:

'Brothers, take me with you to try my luck.'

'You dolt, you go on sitting on the stove, or else go off into the forest to gather mushrooms,' they answered. 'And do not get in our way.'

The two elder brothers mounted their good horses, cocked their hats jauntily, whistled and whooped, and rode off, making the dust fly up in clouds. But Ivan picked up a bridle and went out into the open field. There he called as his father had instructed him:

'Dun horse, magic horse! Come when I call.'

At once a horse galloped up. The earth trembled under its hoofs, flames streamed from its nostrils, smoke rose in columns from its ears. It stood as though rooted to the ground and asked:

'What are your commands?'

Ivan stroked the horse, bridled it, climbed into its right ear and out of its left, and was turned into the most dashing young man one could imagine. Then he mounted the horse and rode off to the tsar's palace. As the dun horse galloped along the earth trembled; it flew over hills and valleys, through woods and forests till they arrived.

When Ivan rode into the tsar's courtyard he found a great number of young men already gathered. In the centre of the courtyard a high tower, twelve logs high, was raised on twelve pillars, and at the very top the princess of matchless beauty was sitting at a little window.

The tsar came out to the courtyard and said:

'If any one of you young men can jump on his horse right up to that little window and kiss my daughter on her lips I will give her to him as his wife with half my kingdom as the marriage dowry.'

So the fine young men began to jump, one after another. But the window was very high, and not one succeeded in reaching it. Ivan's brothers tried too, but they did not even get halfway. At last it was Ivan's turn to make the attempt.

Whooping and whistling, he urged the dun horse into a jump, and failed by only the height of two logs. He turned his horse, flew up a second time, and failed by only one log. So he turned his horse again, circled round the courtyard, urged it on and took the jump at full gallop. Like a flame he flew up to the little window and kissed the princess on her lips as he went past. The princess struck him on his forehead with the ring on her finger, leaving her mark.

Seeing that Ivan had succeeded, everybody shouted:

'Hold him!'

But Ivan had already galloped away, and was nowhere to be found. He galloped into the open field, slipped into the dun horse's left ear and out of its right, and turned back into Ivan the Fool. He let the horse go, and returned home, gathering mushrooms on the way. He bound his forehead with a rag to hide the princess's mark, climbed on to the stove and stretched himself out.

When his brothers rode home they told him where they had been and all they had seen.

'There were some splendid young men there,' they said. 'But one outshone all the

rest. In full gallop he jumped up and kissed the princess on her lips. We saw the direction he had come from, but no one knows where he went.'

From the stove Ivan called down:

'But was not I that handsome young man?'

'Ivan, you are a fool, and you talk like a fool. Sit on the stove and eat your mushrooms,' his brothers answered angrily.

Then Ivan unbound the rag and laid bare the spot on his forehead where the princess had struck him. At once the room was filled with light. His brothers were alarmed, and they shouted at him:

'What are you playing at, you fool? You will set the house on fire.'

So he bound the rag over his forehead again.

Next day the tsar summoned all his princes and noblemen, and even ordinary people, whether rich or poor, old or young, to a banquet. Ivan's brothers also made ready to attend the banquet. So Ivan asked them:

'Take me with you.'

'You would only make the people laugh, stupid!' they answered. 'Sit on the stove and eat your mushrooms.'

The two brothers got on their horses and rode off, but Ivan set out on foot after them. He arrived at the tsar's palace in time for the banquet and seated himself in a distant corner. The princess began to go from one guest to another, offering each a bowl of mead and looking to see if anyone had her mark on his forehead. She passed round all the guests, and finally came to Ivan sitting in the corner. As she approached him her own heart suddenly beat faster. She looked at him; he was smothered in dirt, and his hair was standing on end untidily.

None the less the beautiful princess asked him:

'Whose son are you? Where are you from? Why is your forehead bandaged?'

'I knocked it,' he answered.

She took the rag off his forehead, and at once all the palace was lit up. And she cried out:

'That is my mark. Here is my destined husband.'

The tsar came up, looked at Ivan, and said:

'How can he be your destined husband? He is covered with soot.'

But Ivan said to him:

'Let me go out and wash.'

The tsar gave his permission. Ivan went out into the courtyard and called as his father had instructed him:

'Dun horse, magic horse! Come when I call.'

At once the dun horse came galloping up, making the ground tremble under its hoofs. Flame streamed from its nostrils, smoke rose in columns from its ears. Ivan crawled into its right ear, crawled out of its left ear, and was turned into the handsomest young fellow one ever saw. All the people cried out in astonishment. The tsar gave a banquet and everybody went to the wedding.

Maria Morievna

ONCE UPON A TIME there was a certain prince, named Ivan, who had three sisters: Maria, Olga, and Anna. The time came when their father and mother, the tsar and tsaritsa, both died; and just before gave Ivan their last wishes concerning their three daughters. 'Ivan,' they said, 'if any man comes to you and asks for the hand of one of your sisters in marriage, give her to him. Do not keep any of them with you at home.' After the prince had buried his parents, he sadly went for a walk with his sisters in their green garden. Suddenly a black cloud overcast the sky, and there was a terrible clap of thunder. 'We had better go home, sisters,' Prince Ivan said. They had hardly entered the palace when they heard another clap of thunder, the ceiling split in two, and a white falcon flew down into their chamber. The falcon beat himself against the floor and changed into a handsome young man. 'Greetings, Prince Ivan,' said the new-comer. 'In former days I came as your guest, but now I have come to ask for the hand of your sister, Princess Maria.'

'If you love my sister,' Prince Ivan answered, 'I have no objection. May God bless her.' Princess Maria was agreeable to the marriage, so the falcon and she celebrated the wedding and he carried her off to his kingdom.

Hour followed hour, day followed day, until a whole year had passed. Then one day Prince Ivan went with his two sisters for a walk in their green garden. Again a black cloud overcast the sky, and with it came a whirlwind and lightning. 'We had better go home, sisters,' said Prince Ivan. They had hardly entered the palace when there was another thunder-clap, the ceiling split in two, and an eagle flew down. He struck himself against the floor and changed into a handsome young man. 'Greetings, Prince Ivan,' he said. 'In past days I came as a guest, but now I have come as a suitor. I wish to marry Princess Olga.' Prince Ivan told him: 'If you love my sister Olga, and if it is her will, she may go with you. I shall have no objection.' Princess Olga agreed and took the eagle for her husband; they were married, and then the eagle caught her up and carried her to his kingdom.

Another year had passed when one day Prince Ivan said to his youngest sister: 'Let

44

us go for a walk in the green garden.' They had been walking for only a little while when there was a clap of thunder, with lightning. 'We had better go home, sister,' said the prince. They returned home, but before they could even sit down there was a thunder-clap, the ceiling parted, and a raven flew down. He beat himself against the floor and changed into a handsome young man: the falcon and the eagle had been good-looking enough, but this raven was even more strikingly handsome. 'Well, Prince Ivan,' he said, 'in past days I came as a guest, but now I have come as a suitor. Give me Princess Anna for my wife.'

'I shall not compel my sister against her will; if you have fallen in love with her, and she with you, she may go with you,' replied Ivan. Princess Anna agreed to be the raven's wife, and he carried her off to his home.

Now Prince Ivan lived alone; and he spent a whole year without seeing his sisters. 'I will go and see how they are getting on,' he said to himself one day. He made ready for the journey, and set out. After travelling some distance he came to a field where a host of soldiers were lying dead. And he called: 'If there is any man left alive here, speak up and tell me: who killed all this mighty force?' Just one man was left alive, and he answered. 'All this mighty force was killed by Maria Morievna, the beautiful queen.' As the prince journeyed farther he came to white tents pitched in a field. And

from one of them the beautiful queen Maria Morievna came to meet him. 'Greetings, Prince,' she said. 'Where are you going, to freedom or slavery?'

'Fine young men do not ride to slavery,' Prince Ivan replied.

'Well, since there is no hurry, be our guest, and enter our tents,' she invited him. The prince was glad of the invitation, and he spent two nights in the queen's camp. He fell in love with her and she with him, and they were married.

The beautiful Queen Maria Morievna took the prince with her to her own country, and they lived happily for some time. But then the queen decided to make war on another country, so she handed over the government of all her lands to Prince Ivan, and told him: 'Ride everywhere, and keep an eye on everything. But one thing you must not do: you must not even look into this boxroom,' and she showed him the door of the boxroom. Unfortunately, the prince could not restrain his curiosity; as soon as the queen had ridden away he ran to the boxroom, opened the door, looked in, and saw Kashchey the Deathless, fettered with twelve chains. When Kashchey saw the prince he pleaded: 'Have pity on me, give me some water to drink. For ten years I have been suffering torments here, being given neither food nor drink. And my throat is quite dry.' So the prince brought him a full bucket of water; he drank it all in one gulp

and asked: 'Give me some more; my thirst cannot be quenched with a single bucketful.' So the prince brought him a second bucketful. Kashchey drank that, and asked for a third. But when he had drunk the third bucketful of water all his former strength was restored, he shook his chains, and snapped all twelve at once. 'Thank you, Prince Ivan,' Kashchey the Deathless said. 'Now you will never see Maria Morievna again any more than you can see your own ears.' He flew out of the window in a fearful gust of wind, overtook the beautiful Queen Maria Morievna on the road, caught her up and carried her off.

The prince, left alone in his palace, wept bitterly over the loss of his beautiful Maria Morievna, but then he decided to go and search for her, and made ready for a long journey. 'No matter what happens,' he declared, 'I shall search till I find Maria Morievna.'

He rode for one day, then a second, and at dawn of the third day he came to a wonderful palace. An oak was standing outside the palace, and in the oak a white falcon was sitting. The falcon flew down from the oak, beat itself against the ground, and turned into a handsome young man. He cried: 'Why, it is my brother-in-law! How is God treating you, Prince Ivan?' Princess Maria, Ivan's sister, heard the shout and ran out. She welcomed Ivan joyfully, asking about his health, and wanting to know all that had happened to him since she left. The prince stayed with his sister and brother-in-law as their guest for three days. But then he told them: 'I cannot stay with you longer; I am looking for my wife, the beautiful Queen Maria Morievna.'

'You will have difficulty in finding her,' the falcon said. 'But leave your silver spoon with us, just in case we can help. We shall look at it and it will remind us of you.' So Prince Ivan left his silver spoon with the falcon and went his way.

He travelled for two days, and at dawn of the third day he saw ahead of him a palace still finer than the falcon's. Outside it was an oak, and in the oak an eagle was sitting.

When it saw Ivan the eagle flew down from the oak, turned into a handsome young man and cried: 'Get up, Princess Olga. Our dear brother Ivan has arrived.' Princess Olga ran out and greeted Ivan joyfully, embracing him, asking after his health and all that had happened to him since her marriage. Prince Ivan spent three days with his sister and brother-in-law, then he said: 'I cannot remain as your guest any longer. I am going to look for my wife, Maria Morievna, the beautiful queen.' The eagle told him, 'You will have difficulty in finding her. But leave your silver fork with us; we shall look at it from time to time to remind ourselves of you.' So the prince gave them his silver fork, said farewell, and rode off on his way.

Two more days he spent on the road, and at the dawn of the third he came to a palace even finer than either of the other two. Outside the palace an oak was growing, on the oak a raven was sitting. When it saw Ivan the raven flew down from the oak, beat against the ground, changed into a handsome young man, and cried: 'Princess Anna! Come quickly, our brother has arrived.' Princess Anna ran out and welcomed her brother joyfully, embracing him and asking after his health and all that had happened to him since she left. Prince Ivan was their guest for three days, then he said: 'Goodbye! I must be on my way to look for my wife, the beautiful Queen Maria Morievna.'

'You will have a hard task finding her,' the raven said. 'But leave your silver snuffbox with us; we will look at it occasionally to remind ourselves of you.' The prince gave them his silver snuffbox, said goodbye, and went his way.

Two more days passed, but on the third he found his way to Maria Morievna. She saw her beloved husband coming, threw herself into his arms, and wept bitterly as she said: 'Ah, Prince Ivan, why did not you listen to me? Why did you look into the box-room and release Kashchey the Deathless?'

'Forgive me, Maria Morievna.' he pleaded. 'Do not reproach me with the past, but ride away with me before Kashchey the

Deathless sees us. Perhaps we shall get too far for him to overtake us.' So they made ready and rode away. Kashchey was out hunting; as he returned home late in the afternoon his good horse stumbled under him. 'What is the matter with you, you old nag?' he demanded. 'What made you stumble? Have you scented some misfortune?' The horse answered: 'Prince Ivan has come and carried off Maria Morievna.'

'But can we overtake them?' Kashchey asked.

'You could sow your wheat, wait for it to grow, you could harvest it and thresh it, grind it into flour, bake bread from it in five ovens, and eat the bread, and only then set out in pursuit. And even so we would overtake them,' said the horse. So Kashchey galloped after and overtook Prince Ivan. 'Well,' he said to the prince, 'this first time

I forgive you because of your kindness in giving me water to drink. And I will forgive you a second time. But if it happens a third time look out for yourself: I shall cut you into little pieces.' He took Maria Morievna from the prince and carried her off, while Ivan sat down on a stone and wept.

He wept until he had no more tears to weep, then he set out again to carry off Maria Morievna. When he arrived Kashchey the Deathless happened to be out hunting. 'Let us go, Maria,' said the prince. But she answered: 'Ah, dear Ivan, he will overtake us.'

'Let him,' he said, 'we shall at least spend an hour or two together.' And as he insisted, they made ready and rode away. In the late afternoon Kashchey the Deathless was riding back home when his horse stumbled under him. 'What is the matter with you, old nag?' he demanded. 'Why did you stumble? Have you perhaps scented some misfortune?'

'Prince Ivan has come and carried Maria Morievna away,' the horse answered. 'Then can we overtake them?' he asked. 'You could sow barley, wait for it to grow, you could harvest and thresh it, brew beer from it, drink the beer till you were drunk, sleep it off completely and then ride in pursuit: and still we would catch them.' So Kashchey galloped after Prince Ivan, caught up with him, and said: 'Do you not remember my telling you would no more see Maria Morievna than you can see your own ears? But I forgive you this second time.' He took Maria Morievna from him and carried her off.

Prince Ivan was left alone; he wept and wept, but then he went back a third time for Maria Morievna. Kashchey happened to be out when he arrived. 'Let us go, Maria,' he pleaded. 'Ah, Ivan' she answered, 'but he will overtake us, and then he will cut you into pieces.'

'Let him!' said Prince Ivan. 'I cannot live without you.' So they made ready and rode away. As Kashchey the Deathless was riding home that afternoon his good horse stumbled. 'What made you stumble?' he asked. The horse answered: 'Prince Ivan has arrived and carried off Maria Morievna yet again.' Kashchey did not stop to ask whether the horse could overtake them: he galloped after Ivan and Maria, caught up with them, cut Ivan into little pieces with his sword, and put the pieces into a tarred barrel. Then he ringed the barrel with iron hoops and flung it into the blue sea. And he carried Maria Morievna back to his palace.

At the very moment that Kashchey cut Prince Ivan into pieces the silver articles the prince had left with his sisters were tarnished. 'Ah,' his brothers-in-law said, 'evidently some misfortune has happened to him.' The eagle flew up and saw the barrel floating in the sea, and dragged it on to the shore. The falcon flew to fetch spring water, and the raven for still water. Then all three flew to the spot where the barrel was

lying, broke it open, took out the pieces of Prince Ivan, washed them, and put them together as they had been. The raven sprinkled the still water over the pieces, and they grew together and became one whole; the falcon sprinkled the spring water over the body, and Prince Ivan shuddered, sat up, and remarked: 'Why, what a long time I have been asleep!'

'You would have slept even longer if it had not been for us,' his brothers-in-law told him. 'Now come and be our guest.'

'No, dear brothers,' he answered. 'I must go and look for Maria Morievna.'

So he set off once more, reached the palace where she was being held, and asked her: 'Find out from Kashchey the Death-less where he obtained such a splendid horse as he rides.' Maria Morievna waited for a favourable moment, and then asked Kashchey about the horse. And he told her. 'Beyond twenty-seven lands, in the thirtieth kingdom, the farther side of the River of Fire lives a witch, Baba Yaga. She has a mare on which she flies right round the world every day. She has many other re-markable mares too. I worked for her three days as a shepherd. She would not give me one of her mares in payment for my work, but she did give me one small foal.'

'But how did you get across the River of Fire?' Maria asked.

'I have a magic handkerchief. I waved it three times to the right and a very high bridge arose, which the fire could not reach.' Maria Morievna listened carefully to what he said, and told Prince Ivan all she had found out. She managed to get hold of the magic handkerchief without Kashchey knowing, and gave it to the prince.

So Prince Ivan used the handkerchief to cross the River of Fire, and hurried on to find the witch, Baba Yaga. He walked on and on for a long time without finding any-thing to eat or drink. At last he happened to see a bird with her little chicks, and he told her: 'I must eat one of your chicks.'

'Please do not do that, Prince Ivan,' she pleaded. 'Do not take any of my chicks, and sooner or later I shall be of service to you.'

So he went on. A little later, in the forest he saw a beehive, and he said: 'I will take some of the honey.' But the queen bee pleaded: 'Do not take any of my honey, Prince Ivan. Then some day I shall be of service to you.' So he did not touch the honey, and walked on. He saw a lioness with her cub coming towards him, and said: 'At any rate I must eat that cub. I am so hungry that I could eat anything.'

'Please do not hurt my cub, Prince Ivan,' the lioness pleaded. 'Some time or other I may be of service to you.'

'All right, just as you wish,' he said.

So he wandered on, feeling terribly hungry, until he came to the house of the witch, Baba Yaga. The house was surrounded by twelve poles; on eleven of the poles human heads were impaled, and only one pole was without a head. He went up to the witch and said: 'Greetings, Grannie.'

'Greetings, Prince Ivan,' she answered. 'Why have you come to visit me, of your own free will or out of necessity?'

'I have come to earn an heroic horse from you,' he told her.

'By all means, Prince. And you will not have to serve me for a year, only three days altogether. If you graze my mares without losing one of them I will give you a horse fit for any hero. But if you fail, you must not mind if I stick your head on that empty pole.' The prince agreed to these terms, the witch gave him food and drink, and told him to begin working, but he had hardly driven the mares out into the field when they kicked up their hoofs and scattered all over the meadows; before he had time to look they had all disappeared from sight. He was plunged into despair, sat down on a stone, and began to weep; but he was so tired that he fell asleep. The sun was setting when he was awakened by the bird whose chick he had spared. 'Get up, Prince Ivan,' she said. 'And do not worry: the mares are already at home.' So the prince got up and went back to the witch's house. There he found her shouting and screaming at the mares: 'Why have you come back home?'

'But what else were we to do?' they asked. 'Birds came flying from all over the world and all but pecked out our eyes.'

'In that case, tomorrow do not scatter over the meadows, but run into the dense forest,' she told them.

Prince Ivan had a good sleep that night, and in the morning the witch told him: 'Look to it, Prince! If you do not guard my mares properly, if you lose even one, your fair head will decorate that pole.' He went to the mares and drove them out into the field. But they immediately flourished their tails and scattered about the dense forest. In his despair the prince sat down on a stone and wept. But he felt tired after chasing the mares, and he fell asleep. As the sun was setting beyond the forest the lioness ran up to him and awakened him. 'Go home, Prince Ivan,' she told him. 'The mares are

all rounded up.' So the prince went back to the house. There he found the witch raging and storming even more than before at the mares. 'Why have you come back home?' she demanded.

'But what else could we do?' they asked. 'Savage beasts from all over the world came running after us and all but tore us to pieces.'

'Well then,' she said, 'tomorrow you must run right into the blue sea.'

The prince had another good sleep that night, and next morning the witch sent him out a third time to guard the mares. 'But if you lose one of them,' she warned him, 'your head will decorate the pole.' As soon as he drove the mares into the field they tossed their manes and disappeared from his sight, for they ran right into the blue sea. There they stood up to their necks in the water. Prince Ivan was in despair; he sat down on a stone and wept. And as he wept he fell asleep. The sun was setting when the queen bee flew up and told him: 'Get up, Prince. All the mares are rounded up. But when you go back, do not let the witch see

you. Go into the stable and hide behind the
mangers. In there you will see a sorry-
looking foal rolling in the dung. Steal him,
and in the dead of night ride away from the
witch's house.'

Prince Ivan rose, went to the stable, and
hid behind the mangers. As he lay there he
heard Baba Yaga shouting and swearing at
her mares: 'What have you come back for?'
she demanded.

'But what else were we to do?' they asked.
'Swarms of bees from all over the world
flew up and stung us until they drew blood.'

The witch went off to bed, and at midnight Prince Ivan took the sorry-looking
foal, saddled it, and galloped off to the River
of Fire. He rode up to the river, and waved
Kashchey's handkerchief three times to the
right. Suddenly a magnificent, lofty bridge
hung over the river, appearing from nowhere. He rode across the bridge, and
waved the handkerchief to the left. But he
waved it only twice, and a very slender
bridge was left across the river. On the
farther side, the prince gave the foal a good
feed of grass in a green meadow, and it grew
into a magnificent horse.

Next morning when the witch woke up
she could not find the prince, and soon discovered that the foal had gone. So she
rushed in pursuit, riding in her iron mortar
and urging it on with a pestle, sweeping

away her tracks behind her with a besom.
She rode up to the River of Fire, looked at
the bridge, and thought: 'That is a good
bridge!' But when she rode on to the bridge
and reached the middle it collapsed, and she
fell headlong into the River of Fire. There
she met with a fearful death.

Meanwhile, Prince Ivan rode once more
to rescue Maria Morievna; she saw him
coming, ran out, and flung her arms round

his neck. 'How have you been restored to life?' she asked him. He told her all that had happened to him, and said: 'Now ride home with me.'

'But I am afraid, Prince Ivan,' she answered. 'If Kashchey overtakes us he will cut you into little pieces again.'

'He will not overtake us this time,' he told her. 'Now I have a magnificent horse, good enough for any hero; it flies along like a bird.' So they mounted the horse and rode away.

As Kashchey the Deathless was returning home in the afternoon his horse stumbled. 'What is the matter with you, old nag?' he asked it.

'Prince Ivan has come again and carried off Maria Morievna,' the horse told him.

'But can we overtake them?' he asked.

'Goodness knows!' the horse answered. 'Prince Ivan now has a horse fit for any hero, and it is even better than me.'

'No, I cannot endure the thought of his getting away,' Kashchey said. 'We will go in pursuit.' He rode long, he rode hard, and he caught up with Prince Ivan, sprang to the ground, and was about to cut him down with his sharp sword. But Ivan's horse let fly with its hind hoofs, kicked Kashchey with all its force and smashed in his head. Ivan finished him off with a club. Then the prince made a pile of wood, set fire to it, burnt Kashchey the Deathless on the pyre, and scattered the ashes to the four winds.

Maria Morievna seated herself on Kashchey's horse, the prince mounted his, and they rode away to visit first the raven, then the eagle, and then the falcon. At each of the palaces they were welcomed joyfully. 'Ah, Prince Ivan,' his sisters and brothers-in-law said, 'we had given up all hope of ever seeing you again. But now we can see why you exposed yourself to such great danger. You could search all over the world for another queen as beautiful as Maria Morievna, and you would never find one.' At each of the three palaces they feasted and banqueted, and then they rode off to their own kingdoms. When they arrived home they once more lived in happiness.

The Swan-Geese

MANY YEARS AGO, long before you or I can remember, there was a poor peasant, with a daughter and a baby son. The father and mother had to go out to work, and when the daughter was old enough they left her in charge of the baby. One day the mother said to her daughter: 'My dear, Daddy and I are going to work today, so you must look after your little brother. Now do not go outside the yard; be a good girl, and we will buy you a kerchief for your head.'

Then the parents went off to work for the

day. But the girl soon forgot what she had been told: she put her baby brother down on the grass under their cottage window, and ran out into the village street to play. While she was away swan-geese flew up from beyond the forest, seized the baby boy in their beaks, and carried him off.

When the girl returned home she could not find her brother anywhere. She looked everywhere for him, calling to him, but there was no answer, and it was all in vain. The tears rolled down her face, for she was fond of her brother.

In her search for him she ran out beyond the village, and noticed the swan-geese flying a long way off, till they disappeared beyond the dark forest. Then she guessed that they had carried off her brother; she had often been told of the wicked tricks these birds played, and how they carried off little children.

She ran after them to try to overtake them. And as she ran, suddenly she saw a great Russian stove standing in her path.

'Dear stove,' she said, 'tell me where the swan-geese have gone.'

'Inside me you will find a cake made of

rye flour,' the stove answered. 'Eat it up and I will tell you.'

'I am not eating your rye cake,' the girl answered. 'In my father's house we do not even eat cakes made of white flour.'

So the stove refused to tell her. She ran on, and came to a crab-apple tree. She asked the tree:

'Apple-tree, Apple-tree, tell me where the swan-geese have gone.'

'Eat one of my crab-apples and I will tell you,' the tree answered.

'Certainly not,' she said. 'In my father's house we do not even eat the apples in our orchard.'

So the apple-tree would not tell her. The girl hurried on, and came to a river of milk flowing between banks of jelly.

'River of milk, banks of jelly,' she asked, 'where have the swan-geese flown?'

'Eat some of my plain jelly and milk and I will tell you,' the river answered.

But the girl retorted: 'In my father's house we do not even eat cream.'

She spent a lot of time running through the fields and forests. The day drew on to evening, and it looked as though she would have to return home without her brother. But suddenly she saw a little hut standing on a chicken leg, and turning round and round. In the hut an old woman, Baba

Yaga, was spinning thread. And on a bench the girl's baby brother was sitting playing with silver apples.

The girl went into the hut, and said:

'Good evening, Grannie.'

'Good evening, Girl,' the witch replied. 'What have you come here for?'

'I have had to run through mosses and marshes, and I am soaking wet. Can I come in to warm myself?'

'Sit down then and take over my spinning,' the witch told her. She gave the girl the spindle, and went out. While she was spinning a mouse ran out from under the stove and said to her:

'Girl, give me some gruel, and I will tell you some good news.'

The girl gave the mouse some gruel, and it said:

'The old witch has gone out to heat the bathhouse. When it is hot she will wash you then put you in the oven and roast you and eat you. And she will go flying about on your bones.'

At this news the girl sat more dead than alive, crying. But the mouse said to her:

'Do not wait a moment. Take your little brother and run away; I will do the spinning.'

The girl at once picked up her baby brother and ran out. After a while the old witch came back from the bathhouse and asked through the window:

'Girl, are you still spinning in there?'

And the mouse answered:

'Yes, I am spinning, Grannie.'

The old witch got the bathhouse very hot and came back to get the girl. But she found no one in the cottage. So she screamed:

'Swan-geese! Fly after them. The girl has carried off her little brother.'

Meanwhile, the sister ran with her brother in her arms until they reached the river of milk. She saw the swan-geese flying after them, and she said:

'Little river, dear mother river, hide me!'

'Then eat some of my plain jelly with milk,' the river answered.

The girl ate some jelly and milk, and said 'thank you'. So the river concealed them both under its bank of jelly. The swan-geese did not see them, and they flew past. The sister picked up her baby brother and set off again as fast as she could run. But she saw that the swan-geese had turned back, and were flying towards them. In a moment they would see the two children. But by now they had reached the crab-apple tree, and the girl cried:

'Apple-tree, dear apple-tree, hide us!'

'Eat some of my crab-apple,' said the tree.

The girl hurriedly ate one or two apples, and said 'thank you.' So the apple-tree concealed them in its branches, covering them with leaves. The swan-geese did not see them in the tree, and they flew past.

She picked up her brother and started

running again. She ran and ran, and now she had only a short distance to go. But the swan-geese noticed them, and with a loud cackling they flew up, beat at the children with their wings, and all but tore the boy out of his sister's arms.

So the girl ran up to the great stove, and cried:

'Dear stove, do hide us.'

'Then eat some of my rye cake,' the stove told her.

She hurriedly ate some rye cake, and dived with her brother into the stove oven. The swan-geese flew round and round, screaming and flapping their wings; but at last they had to fly off without the children, back to the old witch.

The girl said 'thank you' to the stove and ran all the way home, with her brother in her arms.

And their father and mother returned home at that very same moment.

'Go to "I do not know where" "I do not know what"'

ONCE UPON A TIME there was a tsar who had never married. Among his servants was one named Andrew who was a huntsman. He walked about all one day, but was unlucky and found nothing. As evening was coming on, he turned back, in despair of bringing back any game. Then he saw a turtle-dove sitting in a tree.

'I will shoot her, at any rate,' he thought.

So he shot and wounded the dove; it fell out of the tree on to the hard ground. The hunter picked it up, and was about to wring its neck and put it in his bag when it spoke to him in a human voice:

'Do not kill me, hunter Andrew, but carry me home alive, and put me in the window. And then watch. When you see I am dozing beat me hard with your right hand and you will win great happiness for yourself.'

Andrew was astonished: the dove looked quite an ordinary bird, yet here it was talking with a human voice. So he decided to take it home. He set it in the window, and stood waiting and watching.

In quite a short time the dove tucked its head under its wing and began to doze. He remembered what it had told him, and struck it hard with his right hand. The dove fell to the ground and turned into a maiden, Princess Maria; she was so beautiful that you could only think of her as in a dream. She said to Andrew:

'You have been able to catch me; now see if you can keep me. We will have a quiet little feast together, and then we will get married.'

Andrew married Princess Maria and they lived together very happily. But he did not overlook his service to the tsar: each morning before dawn he went into the forest, shot game, and carried it to the palace kitchen.

They had not been married long when Princess Maria said to Andrew:

'You are very poor, Andrew.'

'Yes, I am.'

'Well, get hold of a hundred roubles from somewhere, buy some silk threads with it, and I will soon make things better for us.'

Andrew did as she suggested, went to his friends and others of the tsar's servants, borrowed a couple of roubles from one, and a rouble from another, until he had the hundred roubles. Then he bought a quantity of silk threads and took them home to his wife. She took the threads and said to him:

'Now go to bed. You will feel fine after a good sleep.'

So Andrew went to bed, but Maria sat down to weave. All night she wove, and by dawn she finished a carpet the like of which had never been seen before. On it the whole of the kingdom was embroidered, with towns and villages, forests and harvest fields, birds in the sky, animals on the hills, and fishes in the sea. And the sun and the moon shone in the sky above the kingdom.

When Andrew awoke Princess Maria gave the carpet to him and told him:

'Take it to the shops and sell it to a merchant. Only beware of one thing: you must not fix your price, but take whatever they offer.'

He took the carpet, hung it over his arm, and went off to the shopping arcade. There a merchant hurried up to him and asked:

'My good sir, how much are you asking for your carpet?'

'You are a merchant,' said Andrew. 'You name your price.'

The merchant stood thinking for quite a time, but found it impossible to price the carpet. Another merchant came and joined

and bring me

him, and then another. In the end quite a crowd of merchants was gathered, examining the carpet and marvelling at the beauty of its workmanship. But not one of them could think what price to offer.

Just then one of the tsar's counsellors drove past the arcade. He was curious to know what the merchants were arguing about, so he got out of his carriage, pushed through the crowd, and said:

'Good morning, merchants and visitors from overseas. Why are you arguing?'

'Why, we cannot decide on a price for this carpet,' they answered.

The tsar's counsellor looked at the carpet, examined it, and was astonished beyond words at its beauty. So he turned to Andrew, and asked:

'Tell me the real truth, hunter; where did you get hold of such a carpet?'

'My wife wove it,' said Andrew.

'And how much do you want for it?'

'I really have no idea. My wife told me I was not to bargain over it. We would take whatever we were offered.'

'Well then,' said the counsellor. 'Here is ten thousand roubles for it.'

Andrew took the money, handed over the carpet, and went home. Meanwhile, the counsellor drove to the tsar's palace and showed his master the carpet. The tsar looked at it and saw that it pictured all his kingdom as though it were set out on his palm. And he gasped:

'Say what you like, counsellor, I am not letting you have this carpet back.'

He took twenty thousand roubles out of his purse and handed them to the counsellor. The counsellor took the money, for he thought: 'Never mind; I will order myself another, even finer.' He went back to his carriage, drove to the village where Andrew lived, sought out the hunter's cottage, and knocked at the door. Princess Maria opened it. The counsellor took one step across the threshold, but then he stood speechless, completely forgetting his errand: the woman he saw at the door was so beautiful that he could not take his eyes off her. He would have gone on staring at her for ever. Princess Maria waited for him to speak and say what he wanted, but as he said nothing she turned him round by the shoulder, pushed him outside, and shut the door. Then he pulled himself together and reluctantly went back home. But from that moment he hardly ate or drank, for he could not get the hunter's beautiful wife out of his mind.

The tsar noticed his abstracted behaviour, and asked him what was the matter. The counsellor told him:

'I have seen a certain hunter's wife, and now I cannot stop thinking of her. I do not want to eat or drink, and no potion can cure me.'

On hearing this story the tsar decided that he, too, must see the hunter's wife. He dressed himself in ordinary clothes, rode to the village, found the cottage where Andrew the hunter lived, and knocked at the door. Princess Maria opened it. The tsar put one foot across the threshold, but could not take another step. He was struck dumb: before him stood a woman of unbelievable beauty.

Princess Maria waited for him to say what he wanted. But as he did not speak she turned him round by the shoulder, pushed him out, and closed the door.

The tsar felt a chill at his heart. 'Why am I still a bachelor,' he thought. 'Now if I could marry a beauty like her! She has no right to be a hunter's wife; she was destined from birth to be a tsar's bride.'

He returned to his palace, thinking evil thoughts. How could he marry a woman who already had a husband living? At last he summoned the counsellor, and said:

'Think of a way of getting rid of Andrew the hunter. I intend to marry his wife. If you think of something I will reward you with a gift of towns and villages and gold from my treasury. If you do not I will remove your head from your shoulders.'

The counsellor was downcast; he went away with head hanging. In his dejection he turned into a tavern to have a glass of wine. One of the regular customers, a man in a ragged coat, hurried up to him, and asked:

'Counsellor, what is making you look so miserable?'

'Get away, you drunken fellow,' the counsellor answered.

'Do not turn me away, but buy me a glass of wine. Then I will suggest something that may help you.'

So the counsellor bought him a glass of wine and told him all his troubles. The man said:

'To get rid of Andrew the hunter is easy enough; he himself is a simple soul, but his wife is very clever. However, we will think of a riddle that even she will not be able to solve. Go back to the tsar and tell him to send Andrew to the other world, to find out how the tsar's dead father is getting on. Andrew will go there, but he will never come back.'

The tsar's counsellor thanked the man and hurried off to the tsar to tell him how to get rid of Andrew. The tsar was delighted with the idea, and gave orders for Andrew to be summoned to him. When the hunter arrived the tsar said:

'Well, Andrew, you have served me faithfully and well; now do me one further service: go to the other world and find out how my father is getting on. If you do not go, my sword will sever your head from your shoulders.'

Andrew returned home, sat down on a bench and hung his head dejectedly. So Princess Maria asked him:

'What is the matter, Andrew? Has something gone wrong?'

Then he told her the service the tsar had

ordered him to perform. But she said:

'There is nothing to be sad about. This is not a service, it is quite a little thing. Your real service still lies before you. Go to bed, Andrew. You will feel better after a good sleep.'

Early next morning, as soon as he was awake and dressed, Maria gave him a bag of dry rusks for the journey, and a small gold ring.

'Go to the tsar,' she told him, 'and ask him to let you have his counsellor as companion. Say that you want this because otherwise nobody will believe you have been to the other world. When you set out with your companion throw this ring in front of you; it will act as your guide.'

Andrew took the bag of rusks and the ring, said goodbye to his wife, and went to the tsar to ask him for a travelling companion. Of course, the tsar had to agree, and he ordered his counsellor to go with the hunter.

So they set out on their journey. Andrew

threw the ring in front of him, and it rolled along. They followed it over virgin fields, across mossy marshes, over rivers and lakes. Andrew in front, and the counsellor dragging along behind. They stopped and ate some rusks, then set off again.

At last they came to a dense forest, went down into a deep ravine, and there the ring came to a stop. So Andrew and the counsellor sat down to have some more rusks. As they were sitting there they saw two demons driving an enormous cart loaded with wood. The cart was being drawn by a very old tsar, and the demons were urging him on with cudgels, one on his right, the other on the left. Andrew said to the counsellor:

'Look! Surely that is our late tsar?'

'You are right. It is he.'

So Andrew called to the demons:

'Hey, you devils! Let me have that dead man for just a moment or two at the most. I want to ask him something.'

'Very well,' the demons answered. 'We have no time to wait, while you ask ques-

tions! Are we to haul the wood ourselves?'

'Take a fresh man from me in exchange,' Andrew proposed.

The demons liked the idea, so they unhitched the old tsar, and harnessed up the counsellor in his place. They began to beat him on either side with their cudgels. The counsellor was bent double, but he hauled the cart along.

Meanwhile, Andrew questioned the old tsar about his manner of life.

'Ah, Andrew the hunter,' the tsar replied, 'it is a poor life I live in the other world. Take my son back my greeting and tell him I strictly command him not to offend people, or the same will happen to him.'

He had no time to say any more, for the demons came back with the cart, now empty. Andrew said goodbye to the old tsar, the demons handed back the counsellor, and they set off on their return journey. They arrived in their own country and went straight to report to the tsar. When he saw

Andrew `he rushed at him furiously, demanding:

'By what right have you come back?'

'You gave me a task, and I have performed it,' Andrew answered. 'I have been in the other world and seen your dead parent. He is having a bad time, and he ordered me to give you his greeting and strictly commanded you not to do any offence to people.'

'But how can you prove you have been in the other world?' the tsar asked.

'I can show you the marks on your counsellor's back where demons forced him to work with their cudgels.'

At that the tsar believed Andrew, he could not do otherwise. And he let the hunter go home. But he said to the counsellor:

'Think of a way of getting rid of that hunter, otherwise my sword will get rid of your head.'

The counsellor went away even more dejected than before. He turned into the tavern, sat down at a table and ordered a glass of wine. The tavern's regular customer hurried up to him and asked:

'Why are you so miserable, counsellor? Buy me a glass of wine, and I will give you some sensible advice.'

The counsellor bought him the wine and

a little excursion. Your service still lies ahead of you. You go to bed; you will feel better after a good sleep.'

Andrew went to bed, but Princess Maria went to the local smith and ordered him to forge three iron helmets, a pair of iron tongs, and three rods: one of iron, one of copper, and one of lead. Early next morning she awakened Andrew and told him:

'Here are three helmets, a pair of tongs, and three rods. Journey across twenty-seven lands to the thirtieth kingdom. When you have only three miles left to go you will feel a great desire to lie down and have a nap; that will be the story-telling cat trying to make you go off to sleep. But do not let him do it; swing your arms hard, drag your feet along the ground, and to keep awake even roll along if you feel it necessary. If you fall asleep, the story-telling cat will kill you.'

After fixing in his memory all his wife had told him to do, Andrew set out on his journey. A story is soon told, but a journey takes longer. At last he arrived at the thirtieth kingdom. When he was three miles away he began to feel very sleepy. So he set the three iron helmets on his head, swung his arms vigorously, dragged his feet along the ground, and at times even lay down and rolled along. Thus, somehow or other he overcame his drowsiness and came to a very tall pillar, on which the story-telling cat was sitting.

When the cat saw Andrew it snorted, snarled, and jumped from the pillar right on to his head. It smashed one of the iron helmets, then the second, and was about to deal with the third when the hunter seized it in the tongs, dragged it to the ground and belaboured it with the rods. He started beating with the iron rod, but it broke; then he beat the cat with the copper rod, and this, too, broke. So he turned to beating it with the leaden rod. The leaden rod bent, but it did not break; it curled round the cat's back. So Andrew beat away, and the cat began to tell him stories. Stories about priests, about deacons, and about priests' daughters. But the hunter did not listen, he only went on beating.

told all his troubles. The man told him:

'Go back and tell the tsar to give the hunter the following task. It is hard enough to think of it, far harder to do it. He must send him beyond twenty-seven lands, to the thirtieth kingdom, to bring back the story-telling cat.'

The counsellor hurried back to the tsar and told him the task he should set Andrew to ensure he never came back. The tsar sent for the hunter and told him:

'Now, Andrew, you have done me one service, now do me another. Go to the thirtieth kingdom and bring me back the story-telling cat. Otherwise my sword will remove your head.'

Andrew went back home feeling very miserable, and told his wife what the tsar had commanded him to do.

'There is nothing to worry about,' Princess Maria said. 'That is not a service, only

The cat began to grow weak, and it saw that all its talk was of no use. So it tried to plead with Andrew:

'Leave me alone, my good man,' it said, 'and I will do all you want.'

'But will you come with me?' Andrew demanded.

'I will go wherever you wish.'

So Andrew set off home, leading the cat behind him. When he arrived in his own country he took the cat to the palace and said to the tsar:

'Well, I have performed my service, I have brought you the story-telling cat.'

But the tsar was alarmed, and he asked:

'Please, Andrew, keep the cat shut up in a cage.'

So Andrew shut the cat in a cage, and went home to his princess wife. And now for a time he was left in peace to live happily with Maria. But the tsar had not forgotten her, and his desire for her increased even more. At last he summoned the counsellor:

'Think up whatever you like,' he said. 'But get rid of Andrew. Otherwise my sword will get rid of your head.'

This time the counsellor knew what to do. He went straight to the tavern, found the man he had seen before, and asked him to save him by giving him some good advice. The man drank his glass of wine, wiped his whiskers, and said:

'Go to the tsar and tell him to send Andrew to I do not know where and to bring back I do not know what. Andrew simply cannot do that, and so he will never return.'

The counsellor hurried back to the tsar and told him what to do. The tsar sent for Andrew.

'You have done me two services,' he said. 'Now do me a third. Go to I do not know where and bring me back I do not know what. If you succeed, I will reward you with royal munificence; but if you fail, my sword will remove your head.'

Andrew went home, sat down on a bench, and burst into tears. Princess Maria asked him:

'You seem unhappy, my dear. Have you run into some more trouble?'

'Ah, Maria,' he answered; 'it is your beauty that has brought all these troubles upon me. Now the tsar has ordered me to go to I do not know where and bring him back I do not know what.'

'Now that is a real service,' Maria said. 'But do not worry; you go to bed. You will feel better after a good sleep.'

Andrew went to bed, but the princess waited till nightfall; then she opened her book of magic and read and read. But at last she put it aside and clutched her head: there was nothing in it that helped in regard to the tsar's task. So she went to the door, took out a handkerchief, and waved it. All sorts of birds came flying to the door, and all sorts of animals came running. Princess Maria asked them:

'Animals of the forest, you go rummaging everywhere; birds of the air, you go flying everywhere. Tell me, have you ever heard how to get to I do not know where and to bring back I do not know what?'

But the animals and birds answered:

'No, Princess Maria; we have never heard of such a thing.'

She waved her handkerchief again, and the animals and birds vanished as if they had never been. Then she waved it once more, and two giants appeared before her.

'What can we do for you, Princess?' they asked.

'My faithful servants, carry me to the middle of the ocean.'

The giants picked her up and carried her to the ocean, waded into it and stood in the middle, in the very deepest part. They

stood there like two pillars, holding her in their arms. Princess Maria waved her handkerchief, and all the sea serpents and fishes came swimming up to her.

'Sea serpents and fishes,' she said, 'you swim everywhere, you visit all the islands. Have you ever heard how to get to I do not know where and to bring back I do not know what?'

'No, Princess Maria,' they answered. 'We have never heard of such a thing.'

Now Maria was very despondent, and she ordered the giants to carry her back home. They took her back to Andrew's cottage and set her down at the door.

Next morning she made preparations for her husband's journey, gave him an embroidered towel and a ball of thread.

'Throw the ball in front of you,' she told him. 'Follow it wherever it rolls. But remember, wherever you get to, if you wash never use anybody else's towel; always wipe yourself with mine.'

Then Andrew said goodbye to the princess, bowed in all four directions, and went out through the gate. He threw the ball in front of him, and it started to roll. Wherever it rolled, he followed.

A story is soon told, but such a journey is not quickly ended. Andrew wandered through many countries and kingdoms, following the ball. It rolled along in front of him, and the thread unwound from it until it grew quite small, no bigger than a hen's head. Then it grew so small that Andrew could not even see it on the road. But then he came to a forest, and saw a little hut standing on a chicken leg.

'Little hut, little hut,' he said; 'turn your front to me, your back to the forest.'

The hut turned round, Andrew went in, and saw a grey-haired old woman sitting on a bench and tousling a bunch of flax. When she saw Andrew she exclaimed:

'Why, whoever saw or heard a Russian soul before? But today a Russian himself has arrived. I shall roast you in the oven and eat you, and go for a ride on your bones.'

'What, you old witch, eat a traveller?' Andrew answered. 'A traveller is nothing

but skin and bones! First get a bath ready, wash me, and steam me, and then you can eat me.'

So the old witch did. Andrew had a bath, steamed himself, washed himself, took out the towel his wife had given him and started to dry himself. The old witch asked him in surprise:

'Where did you get that towel from? My daughter embroidered it.'

'Your daughter is my wife; she gave it to me,' the hunter told her.

'So you are my darling son-in-law,' the witch said in delight. 'I must make a feast ready for you.'

She bustled about, getting supper ready, and set all sorts of food, wines, and meads, on the table. Andrew was not proud; he was hungry, and he sat down at the table and set to work. The old witch sat down beside him and asked how he had come to marry Princess Maria and whether they were happy together. He told her all his story: how he had married Maria, and how the tsar had sent him to I do not know where to bring back I do not know what.

'Now if you could only help me, Mother,' he ended.

'Ah, my dear son-in-law, even I have never heard of that strange wonder. Only one old frog may know of it; she has lived in the marsh for three hundred years. Well, do not worry; go to bed, you will feel better after a good sleep.'

So Andrew went to bed. But the old witch took two birch besoms, flew to the marsh and called:

'Dear Grannie, dear Froggie, are you still alive?'

'Yes, I am,' the frog answered.

'Then come out of the marsh to me.'

The old frog came jumping out of the marsh, and the witch asked her:

'Do you know where I do not know where is?'

'Yes, I do.'

'Be so kind as to tell me. My son-in-law has been given the task of going to I do not know where and bringing back I do not know what.'

'I would show him the way,' the frog replied. 'But I am too old: I could never jump all that distance. However, if your son-in-law will carry me to the River of Fire in some fresh milk straight from the cow, I will tell him.'

The old witch picked up the old frog, hurried home, milked the cow straight into a bucket, put the frog in it, and next morning awakened Andrew.

'Now, my dear son-in-law, listen to me,' she said. 'Get up and dress, and take this bucket of fresh milk. In the milk is a frog. Get on my horse, and he will carry you to the River of Fire. Leave the horse there and take the frog out of the bucket; she will tell you what to do.'

Andrew dressed at once, took the bucket, and seated himself on the witch's horse. Then the horse galloped to the River of Fire. No animal can jump across that river, and no bird can fly over it.

Andrew slipped off the horse, and the frog said to him:

'My good young man, take me out of the bucket; we have got to go across the river.'

So Andrew took the frog out of the bucket and set her on the ground.

'Now, my good young man,' said the frog, 'seat yourself on my back.'

'But how can I?' said Andrew. 'You are so small I am afraid I shall squash you.'

'Do not be afraid, you will not squash me. Get on and hold me tight.'

So Andrew seated himself on the frog. And she began to puff herself up. She swelled and swelled, until she was as big as a haycock.

'Are you holding on tight?' she asked Andrew.

'Very tight, Grannie,' he assured her.

So she puffed herself up even more, and she swelled till she was higher than the dark forest. Then she jumped. She sprang right over the River of Fire, carried Andrew to the farther bank, and then made herself small again.

'Now, young man,' she said, 'follow that path, and you will come to a tower; it is not really a tower, but a hut. And it is not really

a hut, but a shed. And it is not really even a shed. Anyhow, go inside and hide behind the stove. There you will find I do not know what.'

Andrew followed the path, and came to the tower which was really a hut which was really a shed. It had no windows or steps. He went inside and hid behind the stove. After a while he heard a knocking sound, as loud as thunder, coming through the forest, and a little man, no bigger than a thumb, with a beard down to his waist, entered the hut and shouted:

'Hey, Cousin Nahum, I am hungry.'

The moment he shouted a table appeared from I do not know where. It was already laid. On it was a keg of beer and a whole roast ox. Beside the meat lay a sharp knife. The thumb-sized man with a beard down to his waist seated himself at the table, picked up the sharp knife and carved the ox, dipping the pieces of meat in garlic, eating it, and praising the cook. He finished off the ox down to the last little bone, and drank all the keg of beer. Then he shouted:

'Hey, Cousin Nahum, take away the leavings.'

And at once the table vanished as if it had never been. Even the bones disappeared, even the keg. Andrew waited till the little man went out. Then he came from behind the stove, summoned up his courage, and called:

'Cousin Nahum, give me some food, I am hungry.'

He had hardly got the words out when a table appeared from I do not know where, and on it were all sorts of things to eat: appetisers and desserts, wine, and mead. He sat down at the table, and said:

'Cousin Nahum, come and sit with me, and we will eat and drink together.'

A voice answered him:

'Thank you, my good man. I have worked here for very many years, but never even been offered a burnt crust. And you have invited me to sit with you at the table.'

Andrew looked all around him in astonishment. There was no one to be seen, yet the food on the table was disappearing as though it were being swept away with a broom. The wine and mead poured themselves into the glasses, and the glasses jumped up, jumped up, and jumped again until they were empty. So Andrew asked:

'Cousin Nahum, let me have a look at you.'

'No,' the voice answered. 'No one can see me; I am I do not know what.'

'Cousin Nahum, would you like to work for me?' the hunter asked again.

'Of course I should. I can see you would treat me well.'

So they both ate their fill, and then Andrew said:

'Well, clear everything away, and come along with me.'

The table and everything on it vanished. Andrew went out of the hut to start on his way back. At the door, he looked round, and asked:

'Cousin Nahum, are you with me?'

'Yes, I am here,' the voice answered. 'Never fear; I shall not leave you.'

When Andrew got back to the River of Fire he found the frog waiting for him. She asked him:

'My good young man, have you found I do not know what?'

'Yes Auntie, I have.'

'Then seat yourself on my back,' she told him.

He perched himself on her back, and she began to puff herself up. She swelled and swelled until she was as big as the highest tree. Then she jumped and carried him safely across the River of Fire. Back on the other side, he thanked the frog and set off to return to his own country. But before he had gone far, he turned round and asked:

'Cousin Nahum, are you here?'

'I am here,' came the voice. 'Never fear; I shall not leave you.'

So Andrew kept walking on. But it was a long road, and his feet grew very tired, his arms hung helplessly.

'Ah!' he said. 'I am terribly tired.

Then Nahum's voice said to him:

'Why not say so long ago? I would have carried you home swiftly.'

And before Andrew could say anything a violent wind snatched him up and carried him away, over mountains and forests, towns and villages, all flashing past beneath him. Then he found himself flying over the deep sea, and he felt afraid. So he called out:

'Cousin Nahum, I should like a rest.'

At once the wind died down, and he began to descend towards the sea. At first as he looked down he could see only water, and he was even more afraid. But then, as he looked again, a little island made its appearance; in the middle of it was a palace with a golden roof, and all round the palace was a beautiful garden. Cousin Nahum said to Andrew:

'The palace is for you. Have a rest, and eat some food. But look out to sea from time to time. You will see three merchant ships come sailing by. Invite the merchants to call on you and show them hospitality. Treat them well, they have three marvels, and you can exchange me for these marvels. Do not be afraid, I will come back to you afterwards.'

Just as Nahum had said, soon after Andrew had eaten and rested, three ships came sailing by from the west. The merchants on board the ships saw the island, and saw that on it was a golden-roofed palace surrounded by a beautiful garden. And they were astonished.

'What is this miracle?' they said to one another. 'We have sailed this way many many times, but we have never seen this island before, only the blue sea. Let us drop anchor and find out what it is all about.'

The three ships dropped anchor, the three merchants got into a little boat, and rowed to the island. Andrew the hunter was already waiting to receive them.

'Welcome, dear guests,' he said and led them into the palace. The merchants could only marvel as they saw the roof of the palace burning like fire, heard the birds singing in the trees, and noticed that remarkable animals were running about the paths. And they turned to Andrew to ask;

'Tell me, my good man, who built this miracle of a palace here?'

'My servant, Nahum, built it all in one night,' he answered. And he called out:

'Hey, Cousin Nahum, get food and drink ready for me and my guests.'

At once a table already laid appeared from I do not know where; it was laden with food and wine, as much as anyone could wish. The merchants could only gasp at the sight.

'My good man,' they said to Andrew, 'let us make a bargain. Let us have your servant, Nahum, in exchange for any marvel you wish. We have three.'

And the first merchant took a cudgel out of his coat and told Andrew: 'You only need to say to this cudgel: "Hey, cudgel, thrash that man for me," and it will start to thrash him. It will smash the ribs of the strongest of men.'

Then the second merchant took an axe from under his coat, turned it with the handle upward, and the axe began to chop. It chopped and chopped, and a ship appeared; it chopped and chopped, and there was another ship. They were complete with sails, with cannon, and manned by brave sailors. The ships sailed along, the guns fired, and the brave sailors waited to be given their orders.

Then the third merchant took a pipe out of his pocket and began to play it. As he piped, soldiers appeared: cavalry and infantry, with horses, guns, and cannon. The soldiers marched about, the band played music, banners fluttered, the cavalry galloped past, and the officers waited to be given their orders. Then the merchant turned the pipe round and blew down the other end, and they all vanished.

But Andrew said:

'You have three very fine marvels, but mine is even more valuable. If you really want to have my servant, I will accept all your three marvels for him.'

'That is asking rather a lot,' the merchants objected.

'As you please; I shall not exchange him for less.'

The merchants thought it over, and discussed it among themselves. 'What do we need the cudgel, axe, and pipe for?' they asked one another. 'We would be better off with Cousin Nahum, he would keep us in food and drink day and night without our having to work at all.'

So they gave Andrew the cudgel, axe, and pipe, and shouted:

'Hey, Cousin Nahum, we are taking you with us. Will you serve us faithfully and truly?'

'Why not?' the unseen Nahum answered. 'It is all the same to me whom I live with.'

So the merchants returned to their ships, and at once began to feast; they ate and drank, and shouted again and again:

'Hey, Cousin Nahum: bring us this, bring us that.'

And they drank and drank until they were so drunk that they fell out of their chairs on to the floor.

Meanwhile, Andrew sat alone in his palace, and felt sorrowful. 'Ah,' he thought aloud, 'where is my faithful servant, Cousin Nahum, now?'

'Here I am,' the voice said. 'What do you want?'

'Cousin Nahum,' Andrew said in delight, 'it is time I went home to my native country, back to my young wife. So carry me home.'

Once more wind snatched him up, and this time it carried him right home to his native village.

But when the merchants woke up after their drunken sleep they thought they would like a drink to clear their heads. So they shouted:

'Hey, Cousin Nahum! Get some food and drink ready for us. And hurry up about it.'

But although they shouted again and again, nothing happened. Then they looked out over the sea and saw that the island had disappeared; where it had been only the blue waves were roaring. And the merchants were upset and furious. 'Some wicked man has cheated us,' they said. But there was nothing they could do about it, so they hoisted sails and sailed off to wherever they were going.

By then Andrew had been carried to his

native land. The wind dropped him down right by his own cottage, only the cottage was not there any longer; all that was left of it was a burnt chimney.

Then Andrew really did feel sad. He was so upset that he walked out of the village to a lonely spot by the blue sea. There he sat down, holding his head between his hands wondering what had happened to his Maria. As he sat, suddenly, from I do not know where, a grey dove flew down beside him, hit the ground hard and turned into his young wife, the princess. He jumped to his feet, they embraced and kissed each other, and then told each other all that had happened since their parting. Maria told her husband:

'Ever since you left home I have been flying as a grey dove about the forests and groves. The tsar sent for me three times. But they could not find me, and so they burnt down our house.'

Then Andrew called:

'Cousin Nahum, would it be possible for you to build a palace for me in this empty spot beside the blue sea?'

'Why ever not?' said Nahum. 'It shall be done at once.'

And before they could look around the palace stood ready for them. It was a splendid palace, better than the tsar's; it

and had brought back I do not know what.

The messengers went hurrying to and fro, asked questions, and reported back to the tsar:

'Andrew the hunter has indeed been to I do not know where and he has brought back I do not know what.'

At that the tsar was really angry. He gave the order for his army to assemble and march to the seashore, to raze the palace to the ground and to put both Andrew the hunter and Princess Maria to a cruel death.

Andrew saw a strong force of soldiers approaching the palace, so he snatched up the axe and turned it with the handle upward. The axe began to chop and chop, and a ship appeared on the sea. It chopped and chopped again, and a second ship appeared. A hundred times it chopped and chopped, and a hundred ships came sailing across the blue sea.

Then Andrew took out the pipe and piped, and an army appeared in front of the palace. There were cavalry and infantry, with guns and banners. The commanders galloped up to the palace steps and stood waiting for his orders. He gave the order for the battle to begin. Music played, drums rolled, and the regiments advanced. The infantry defeated the tsar's soldiers, the cavalry galloped round and took them prisoner. And from the hundred ships cannon opened fire against the tsar's city.

The tsar saw that his soldiers were taking to flight, and he rushed to stop them. But when Andrew saw him he picked up the cudgel and said:

'Now, cudgel, smash the ribs of that tsar.'

The cudgel rolled forward like a wheel, turning over from end to end. It sped across the field, overtook the tsar, and struck him on the forehead, killing him dead.

And that was the end of the battle. The people poured out of the city and asked Andrew the hunter to take over and rule the country.

Andrew did not have to be asked twice. He organised a banquet for all the people, and then, with his wife the Princess Maria, he ruled the kingdom till he was very old.

was surrounded by a green garden, birds were singing in the trees, remarkable animals were running along the paths. Andrew the hunter and Princess Maria entered the palace, sat down at a window, and talked, rejoicing in the sight of each other. So they lived very happily for one day, then a second, and a third.

But on the fourth day the tsar went hunting, rode down to the blue sea, and saw a palace where there had been nothing before.

'What insolent fellow has taken it into his head to build on my land without my permission?' he exclaimed.

Then messengers hurried off to the palace. They found out that Andrew and Maria were living there, and reported the news back to the tsar. At that the tsar was even more furious than before, and he sent messengers to the palace to find out whether Andrew had been to I do not know where

Finist, the White Falcon

A FARMER AND HIS WIFE had three daughters. As the daughters grew up, so their parents grew old, the farmer's wife died. They were all three equally beautiful, but they were very different in their dispositions. The old farmer was comfortably off, and he felt sorry that his daughters now had no mother. And he thought it a good idea to bring some lonely old maid into the home to take charge of the house and domestic affairs. But his youngest daughter, Maria, who was very industrious, said to him:

'You do not need to do that, father. I will look after everything myself.'

But the elder daughters said nothing.

So Maria began to run the house in her mother's place. She could do everything, she was a good manager; what she did not know, she learned by experience, and she was able to manage well. Her father saw how efficient she was, and he was glad she was such a good worker, as well as being as beautiful as a picture. She was good-hearted and of a gentle disposition, and through her goodness she grew in beauty too. Her elder

sisters were very good-looking, but they never felt quite satisfied with their looks, and were always trying to beautify themselves with cosmetics and continually dressing up in fine clothes. They would spend all day making themselves up, yet in the evening they were no prettier than when they first got up in the morning. By the evening Maria was tired, but she knew that the cattle had been attended to, the house was clean and tidy, she had got supper ready, made dough ready for baking next day, and her father would be pleased with her. She looked at her sisters with kindly eyes, and made no comment about their behaviour. But that made her elder sisters even more angry. They could not help thinking that Maria was even prettier in the evening than she had been in the morning; but they had no idea how or why this had come about.

One day their father had to drive to market. And he asked the three sisters:

'What shall I buy for you, my children? What presents shall I bring you?'

'Father,' the eldest daughter said, 'buy

me a shawl, one with many bright colours and embroidered with gold.'

'Buy a shawl for me too, father,' the second daughter said. 'One coloured and embroidered with gold, but I want red to be one of the colours. And buy me a pair of boots with legs of soft leather, and with high heels, so that they clatter as I walk.'

The eldest daughter was annoyed with her sister, for she was of a jealous nature, and so she said to her father:

'Buy me a pair of boots with soft leather legs too, father. The sort with heels that tap as I walk. And buy me a ring set with a stone; after all, I am your eldest daughter.'

The father promised to buy them the presents they had asked for, and turned to his youngest child:

'But why do you not ask for something?' he said.

'But I do not want anything, father,' said Maria. 'I never go out, and I do not need any finery.'

'But that would not be right, Maria dear. How can I leave you without a present? I will buy you some sweets.'

'I do not need any sweets, father. But if you can, buy a feather that has come from Finist the white falcon, if it is not too expensive.'

So the farmer drove off to market. He bought his elder daughters the presents they had asked for, but he could not find a single feather that had come from Finist, the white falcon, though he inquired of all the merchants.

'We have not any such goods,' they told him. 'There is no demand for them.'

He did not want to upset his youngest daughter, his hardworking, intelligent Maria. But he had to return home without buying a feather that had come from the white falcon.

However, Maria was not upset. 'It does not matter, father,' she said. 'You may be able to buy me my feather next time you go.'

Time passed, and the farmer had to drive to market again. And he asked his daughters what he should buy them as presents; he was a good father.

'Last time you bought me a pair of boots, father,' said his eldest daughter. 'So now

get the smith to shoe the heels of my boots with silver tips.'

The second daughter listened to her sister's request, and said:

'Do the same for me, father. Only, heels shod with tips tap, and I should like mine to ring. And so that I do not lose the nails of the silver tips, buy me a little silver hammer which I can use to knock the nails in.'

'And what shall I buy you, Maria?' he turned to his youngest daughter.

'Look to see if you can find a feather from Finist, the white falcon,' she answered.

The old man drove off to market, quickly arranged his business affairs, and bought the gifts for his elder daughters. But although he searched for the feather all day he could not find one anywhere; nobody had such a thing for sale. Once more he had to to return home without a present for Maria. He felt sorry for her, but she only smiled at him, glad just to see him home again.

After some time the farmer had to drive to market again. And, as always, he asked his daughters what he should bring them back as presents.

The eldest daughter thought and thought, but simply could not think of anything she needed. So she said at last:

'Just buy me something or other, father.'

So the second daughter said:

'Buy me something or other too, father. But buy me something else as well.'

'And what shall I bring you, Maria?' he asked.

'Buy me one little feather from Finist, the white falcon,' she said.

So the old farmer drove off to market. He settled his business, bought presents for his elder daughters, but nothing for Maria. Nobody at the market had heard of such a feather.

As he was driving home he saw a very old man, even older than himself and quite decrepit, walking along the road.

'Hallo,' he greeted the old fellow.

'Hallo, my friend,' the man answered. 'But you look sad; what is the trouble?'

'I have good reason to be sad. My youngest daughter has asked me to buy her just one feather from Finist, the white falcon. I have looked for it everywhere, but I cannot find one. And she is such a good daughter, I do not like disappointing her.'

The very old man stood thinking for a moment. Then he said:

'Well, so be it!'

And he untied the neck of his bag and and took out a small box.

'Here, take this box,' he said. 'It contains one little feather from Finist the white falcon. But remember this: I have only one son. You feel sorry for your daughter, and I for my son. He does not want to get married, though it is time he did. And he told me: if someone asks you for this little feather give it to him. It is my bride who wants it.'

The farmer took the box, and the moment the old man had said these words he was no longer standing on the road; he had vanished. For a moment the farmer thought he must have dreamt it all. But in his hand was the box, and it contained just one feather. He looked at the feather: it was

only an ordinary grey wing feather, yet he had not been able to buy it anywhere.

When he arrived home he gave his elder daughters the presents he had bought for them, and to Maria he handed the box containing the grey feather. The elder daughters started dressing up in their finery and laughed at Maria's little box, telling her to stick her sparrow's feather in her hair and adorn herself with it.

Maria did not say anything. But after the others had gone to bed that night she laid the ordinary grey feather in front of her and began to admire it. Then she picked it up, pressed it to herself, stroked it, and accidentally dropped it.

At once she heard a tap at the window. She opened it, and Finist the white falcon flew into the room. He settled on the floor and turned into a handsome young man. Then she closed the window and they began to talk. Late in the night she opened the

window again, the young man stooped down to the floor, turned into the white falcon, and flew off into the azure sky. But he left behind him an ordinary grey feather.

For three successive evenings Maria had a visit from the falcon. During the day it flew high in the sky, over the fields, over the forests, over the hills, over the seas. But late in the evening it flew back to Maria and turned into a handsome young man.

But on the fourth evening the two elder sisters overheard Maria talking quietly to someone, and they caught the strange voice of the young man. Next morning they asked their sister:

'Who were you talking to last night, dear little sister?'

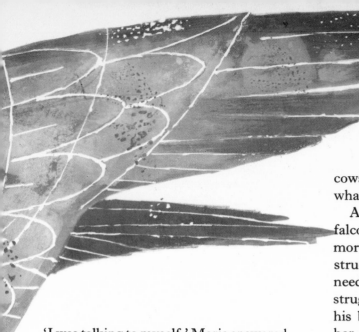

'I was talking to myself,' Maria answered. 'I have not any friends, I am working all day and have no time for talk. So in the evening I talk to myself.'

The elder sisters listened to her story, but they did not believe her. They went to their father and told him:

'Father, Maria has got a boyfriend; she sees him and talks to him at night. We have heard them ourselves.'

But their father told them:

'You had no right to listen. Why should not Maria have a young man? There is nothing wrong in that; she is a good girl. Your turn will come too.'

'But Maria has found a young man out of turn,' the eldest daughter objected. 'I ought to be married before her.'

'That is true, too,' the father reflected. 'But fate does not always arrange things in order. Some girls remain maidens all their lives, while others are sought after when they are quite young.'

But as he said this to his elder daughters, he was thinking: 'Are the words of that old man who gave me the feather coming true, then? There is no harm in that, but I hope Maria has found a good man.'

But the elder daughters had other ideas. As evening came on they removed knife blades from their handles, and stuck the blades into the window frame of Maria's room. And they stuck needle points and pieces of broken glass round the frame. Maria was looking after the cows in the cowshed at the time and knew nothing of what they had done.

As twilight came on Finist the white falcon flew up to Maria's window once more. But as he flew to the window he struck against the sharp knife blades, the needles, and the pieces of broken glass; he struggled and struggled and wounded all his breast. But Maria was worn out with her day's work; she was asleep waiting for him to arrive, and she did not hear him beating at the window.

Then Finist said aloud:

'Farewell, beautiful maiden. If you need me, you must seek me, though I shall be far away. But before you do find me you will wear out three pairs of iron shoes, wear down three steel sticks on the road, and you will eat three loaves of stony bread.'

In her doze Maria heard his words, but she could not get up, or even arouse herself from her sleep. When she woke up next morning her heart was filled with sorrow.

She looked at the window and saw the falcon's blood drying in the sun. And she burst into tears. She opened the window and set her cheek against the spots of blood. Her tears washed away the blood, while she herself became even more beautiful.

She went straight to her father, and said to him:

'Father, do not be cross with me; let me go on a long journey. If I survive we shall see each other again. But if I die, it means it is my fate.'

The old farmer was reluctant to let his favourite, youngest daughter, leave home, but he could not force her to remain. So he let her go.

Maria got the smith to make her three pairs of steel shoes and three iron sticks, and she packed three loaves of stony bread. Then she said farewell to her father and sisters, bowed to her father, and set off

on her journey to find Finist, the white
falcon.

She walked and walked for very many
days, across open country and through dark
forests, and over the high hills. In the fields
the birds sang songs to her; the dark
forests welcomed her; from the tops of the
high hills she admired all the world below.
She walked for so long that she wore out
one pair of steel shoes, wore down one iron
stick on the road, and ate the whole of one
stony loaf. But nowhere could she find
Finist, the white falcon.

So at last she sighed, sat down on the
ground, and was just putting on her second
pair of shoes when she saw a little hut in the
forest. Night was coming on, so she
thought: 'I will go to the hut and ask the
people if they have seen my Finist, the
white falcon.'

She went up and knocked at the door of
the hut. In it lived one solitary old woman,
whether good or bad Maria had no idea.
The old woman opened the door and found
a beautiful girl standing outside. Maria
asked:

'Let me come in, Grannie, to spend the
night.'

'Come in, my little dove, and be my
guest,' the old woman replied. 'But are you
going far, my dear?'

'I do not know whether it is far or near,
Grannie. I am looking for Finist, the white
falcon. Have you ever heard of him?'

'Of course I have. I am very old, I have
lived on the earth a long time, and have
heard of everything. You have a long way to
go yet, my little dove.'

She took Maria in, gave her food and a
night's rest, and said to her next morning:

'You go and see my second sister, my
dear. She is older than I and knows more.

Maybe she will be able to say exactly where your Finist is living. But take this silver distaff and golden spindle as a present from me. When you start to spin the flax a golden thread will be wound on to the spindle. Keep it so long as it is of any value to you, and when you no longer need it give it to someone else.'

Maria took the distaff and spindle, admired them, and thanked the old woman. Then she asked:

'But which way do I go to find your sister, Grannie?'

'I will give you a ball that will roll along by itself. Wherever it rolls, you follow. And if you want to have a rest, just sit down on the grass. The ball will stop and wait for you.'

Maria bowed to the old woman, thanked her again, and went out, following the ball. She walked on for a long time, until she came to a land where the forests were dark and fearful; in the open country the grass

was poor and prickly, the hills she climbed were bare and stony, and no birds were singing in the sky. Now she hurried on faster and faster. She had to change her shoes again; for she wore out the second pair. The second iron stick was worn out too, and she had eaten her second loaf of stony bread.

Ahead of her she saw the black forest, and night was coming on. But in the forest a little light was shining in the window of a small hut. The ball rolled right up to this hut. Maria followed it, knocked at the window, and called:

'Good masters, let me come in for the night.'

An old woman, even older than the one who had given Maria the ball, came to the door. She looked at the girl, and asked:

'Where are you going, my pretty dear? What are you seeking in the world?'

'I am looking for Finist, the white falcon, Grannie,' Maria told her. 'I spent the night with an old grannie in the forest, but though she had heard of Finist, she did not know how I could find him. Maybe, she said, her second sister would know.'

So the old woman invited Maria into her hut. She gave her food and a night's lodging, and next morning she woke her up and said to her:

'You still have to go a long way in your search for Finist. I have heard of him, truly, but I have never seen him. But go along and see our eldest sister; she ought to know all about him. But accept this gift from me. In joy it will be a happy memory for you, and in your need it will be a help.'

She gave Maria a silver dish and a golden egg. Maria thanked her, and went out to follow the ball again.

As she walked on the world around her grew quite strange. Nowhere was there any open country, wherever she turned she saw

only forest. And the farther the ball rolled, the higher grew the trees. The day turned quite dark amid the trees; she could not see the sun in the sky. Yet even through the darkness she went on and on, until her third pair of steel shoes were worn right through, the third stick was worn down, and she had eaten her third loaf to the very last crumb.

She sat down and looked about her, wondering what she was to do. Then she saw that the ball was lying under the tiny window of a small forest hut, so she went up and knocked at the window, and a tottering old woman, the oldest of the three sisters, came to the door.

'Come in, my little dear,' she invited Maria. 'But you must have come a long way. There is nobody living any farther on in this direction; I am the very last. You will have to go in a different direction tomorrow. But who are you and where are you from?'

'I do not belong to these parts, Grannie,'

Maria told her. 'I am seeking Finist, the white falcon.'

The old woman looked at the girl, and said:

'So you are looking for Finist, the falcon? I know him. I have lived a long time on this earth, so long that I know everything, remember everything.'

She gave Maria food, made up a bed for her, and next morning woke her up and told her:

'In past days I never did anybody any good. I live alone in the forest, forgotten by everybody, but I remember everybody. I will tell you where your Finist the white falcon lives. But even when you find him it will be hard for you. Finist is married now, living with his wife and mother-in-law. You have a good heart, so even the hard will prove easy.'

Maria thanked the old woman and bowed down to the ground before her.

'You can thank me afterwards,' the old woman said. 'But here is a little present for you. Accept this golden tambour and needle from me; hold the tambour in your hands, and the needle will do the embroidering by itself. Now go. You will know what you have to do without anyone telling you.'

Now the ball would roll no farther. The old woman came to the door and pointed out the way Maria was to go. And the girl went on, barefoot, just as she was. Now she was beginning to think: 'How shall I ever get there? The ground here is so hard, and so strange.'

But she did not have to go far, for soon she saw a fine courtyard in a glade. In the courtyard was a tower with a carved gateway and window frames of tracery work. A richly dressed, distinguished looking woman was sitting at one window, and when she saw Maria she asked what the girl wanted. Maria remembered that she had nothing on her feet and had eaten her last stony loaf. So she said to the lady:

'Good morning, Mistress. Do you need

a girl who will work for her keep, for clothes and shoes?'

'We could use such a girl,' the lady answered. 'But can you light fires, bring water, and cook dinner?'

'After my mother died I worked for my father; I can do anything in the house.'

'But can you spin, weave, and embroider?'

'Yes, I can,' Maria answered.

'Then go to the servants' kitchen,' the lady told her.

So Maria began to work as a servant in the palace. She was honest and industrious and could do anything that was needed. The mistress kept an eye on her and was delighted to find she had such a willing, good,

and clever worker. The lady told her daughter how pleased she was with the new servant. But the daughter looked at Maria, and sneered:

'Pfooh! She may be pleasant looking, but I am more beautiful than she, and my body is whiter.'

In the evening, when she had finished her work, Maria sat down to spin. She seated herself on a bench, took out the silver distaff and golden spindle, and span. As she span the thread drew away from the flax on the distaff and wound on to the spindle; but it was not a linen, but a gold thread that wound. And as she span she looked into the surface of the distaff, and thought she saw in it Finist, the white falcon; he seemed to be looking at her as though he were alive. Maria gazed at him and said:

'My Finist, my white falcon, why did

you leave me all alone weeping bitterly for you? It was my sisters who shed your blood in order to separate me from you.'

At that moment the mistress's daughter came into the servants' room, and stood a little distance off, watching and listening. Then she went up to Maria, and asked:

'Why are you grieving, girl? And what is that you have in your hands?'

'I am grieving for Finist, the white falcon,' Maria answered. 'And I am spinning thread to weave a towel. Then I shall embroider the towel for Finist, so that he has a towel to wipe his fair face on each morning.'

'Sell me your toy,' the daughter said. 'Finist is my husband, so I myself will spin the thread for him.'

Maria looked at her, put down her golden spindle, and said:

'I have no toy; this is work that I have in my hands. And I must not sell the silver distaff and golden spindle. A good old woman gave them to me.'

The mistress's daughter was offended; she did not want to lose the golden spindle.

'If it is not for sale,' she said, 'I will give you something in exchange for it.'

'Do me just one favour,' Maria said. 'Allow me to take a peep at Finist.'

The daughter thought it over, and finally agreed.

'I will let you, girl,' she said. 'Give me your toy.'

She took the silver distaff and golden spindle; but all the while she was thinking: 'I will not let her look at Finist for long. I will see that nothing happens to him, and give him a sleeping draught. Now we have this golden spindle, mother, and I will grow very rich.'

As night came on Finist the white falcon returned home from the sky, turned into a handsome young man, and sat down to have supper with his wife and mother-in-law. The mistress's daughter sent for Maria to wait at the table, then she could look at Finist, as they had agreed. Maria came in and served at the table, handing round the food and gazing all the time at Finist. But he took no notice of her, he failed to recognise her; she had been worn out by her long journey, and her face was changed through her sorrow for him.

After supper Finist got up and went to his bedchamber. Then Maria said to the wife:

'There are lots of flies in the yard. I will go to Finist in his chamber and drive the flies off him, so that they do not disturb his sleep.'

'Let her go and do it,' the mother-in-law said.

But the young wife thought it over, and finally decided:

'No, let her wait a little.'

She went to her husband, gave him a sleeping potion in his drink, and came back. 'Maybe,' she was thinking, 'this servant girl has some other toy I can get in exchange.' She told Maria:

'You can go now. Go and keep the flies off Finist.'

But when Maria went to his chamber she

forgot all about the flies, for she saw the joy of her heart sleeping a deep sleep. She gazed at him, but could not gaze her fill. She bent close over him, breathing one breath with him, and whispering:

'Wake up, my Finist, my white falcon; it is your Maria who has come to you. I have worn out three pairs of steel shoes, have worn down three iron sticks on the road, and have eaten three loaves of stony bread.'

But Finist was sleeping so soundly, he did not open his eyes or answer one word. His wife, the mistress's daughter, came into the room and asked:

'Have you driven off the flies?'

'Yes,' Maria said. 'They have all flown out of the window.'

Next evening, when Maria had done all her work, she took out the silver dish and rolled the golden egg round it. As the egg rolled round, a second golden egg rolled off the dish. It rolled round a second time, and another golden egg rolled off the dish.

The young mistress was watching, and she came up to Maria and said:

'Why, that is a fine toy. Sell it to me, or let me give you something in exchange.'

'I must not sell them,' Maria answered. 'An old woman gave them to me as a present. And I will give them to you as a present. Here, take them.'

The daughter took the dish and the egg, and was so delighted that she asked:

'But perhaps there is something you need, Maria. Ask whatever you like.'

'I need very little,' the girl answered. 'Just allow me to drive the flies off Finist again tonight, when he goes to bed.'

'Very well,' the young mistress said.

But she was thinking: 'What can happen to my husband just because a servant girl looks at him? And in any case I will send him sound asleep with a potion. He will not open his eyes. And maybe this girl has some other toy I can get.'

Late in the afternoon Finist the white falcon returned as usual from the sky, turned into a handsome young man, and sat down at the table to have supper with his family. His wife sent for Maria to come and wait at the table, to hand round the dishes. Maria handed the dishes round, set out the plates and the cutlery, but did not take her eyes off Finist for a moment. But although he looked at her he did not recognise her.

As she had done the night before, his wife gave him a sleeping potion, and put him to bed. Then she sent Maria to him, ordering her to drive off the flies.

Maria went to Finist, and began calling him and weeping over him. She thought: surely tonight he will wake up and look at me, and recognise his Maria. She called him for a long time, and wiped the tears from her eyes to prevent their falling on his face. But he slept on: he did not wake up and did not open his eyes.

On the third day Maria had done all her work by the evening, and she sat down again on a bench in the servants' room and took out the golden tambour and needle. She held the golden tambour in her hands and the needle embroidered the linen of itself. As she sewed she talked to the work:

'Embroider a beautiful design, embroider it for Finist, the white falcon, so that he has something to delight his eyes.'

The young wife was a little way off. She came into the servants' room, saw the golden tambour and needle in Maria's hands, and noticed that the needle was doing the embroidering without any assistance from Maria. Her heart was filled with envy and greed, and she said to the girl:

'Ah, Maria my dear. Give me that toy, and take whatever you like in exchange. I have the golden spindle, and I spin thread, I weave linen. But I have not a golden tambour and needle, I have nothing to embroider with. If you do not want to let me have them in exchange for something, sell them to me. I will give you a good price.'

'I must not either sell the golden tambour and needle or give them in exchange' Maria said. 'They were given me by the kindest and oldest of the three old women. I will give them to you.'

The young wife took the golden tambour and needle. But she had nothing to give Maria, so she said:

'If you want to, go and drive the flies off

my husband, Finist, tonight. You asked to be allowed to do that yesterday.'

'I will come, if you wish it,' Maria said.

After supper, at first the young wife thought she would not bother to give Finist a sleeping potion; but then she changed her mind, and added it to his drink. 'Why should he look at the girl?' she reflected. 'Let him sleep.'

Maria went to Finist in his bedchamber. But now her heart could be patient no longer. She pressed her cheek against his white breast and lamented:

'Wake up, arouse yourself, my Finist, my white falcon. I have travelled all over the earth on foot to come to you. Three iron sticks have been worn out as I walked, my feet have outworn three pairs of steel shoes, I have eaten three stony loaves. Awake and get up, my Finist, my falcon. Have pity on me.'

But Finist slept on, unaware of her bending over him, not hearing her voice.

She spent a long time trying to awaken him, she wept over him. But he did not stir, the potion was strong. Then one of Maria's scalding tears fell on his chest, and a second dropped on to his face. One tear burned into his heart and the other opened his eyes. And at the same moment he woke up.

'Ah,' he said, 'what was it that scalded me?'

'My Finist, my white falcon,' she answered. 'Awaken to me, it is I who have come to you. Long, long I have sought you, steel and iron have I worn out on the road. They could not endure all the long road to

you, but I have. This is the third night I have called you. But you sleep, you do not wake up, or respond to my voice.'

And then Finist, the white falcon, recognised Maria. He was so happy to see her that at first he could not speak for joy. He pressed her to his white breast and kissed her.

But when he was fully awake he said to her:

'Now, my beautiful, faithful maiden, be my grey dove!'

And at once he turned into a falcon, and Maria became a dove. They flew off into the night sky and flew side by side until daybreak.

As they flew, Maria asked him:

'Falcon, falcon, where are you flying to?

Your wife will be missing you.'

Finist the falcon answered:

'I am flying to you, my beautiful maiden. Anyone who exchanges her husband for a spindle, a dish and a needle does not need a husband; such a wife will never miss him.'

'But then why did you marry her?' Maria asked. 'Was it your wish?'

'It was my wish, but it was not my destiny and my love.'

So they flew on side by side.

But at daybreak they dropped down to the ground. Maria looked about her: she saw her father's house standing just as it always had been. She longed to see her father and at once she was changed into a beautiful maiden. But Finist the white falcon beat himself against the damp earth and was turned into a little feather. Maria picked up the feather, concealed it at her breast, and went to her father. He was overjoyed to see her, and cried:

'Welcome home, my youngest, beloved daughter. I thought you were no longer alive. Thank you for not forgetting your father, for coming back home. Where have you been all this time?'

'Forgive me, father,' she answered.

Now that day happened to be a holiday,

and a great fair was being held in the town. Next morning the farmer made ready to drive to the fair, taking his elder daughters with him to buy themselves presents. And he invited his youngest daughter also to go with them.

'Father,' she answered, 'I am tired after my journey, and I have nothing to wear. I expect everybody at the fair will be wearing their best clothes.'

'But I will get you some fine clothes there, my dear,' her father told her. 'I expect there will be a lot for sale at the fair.'

And her elder sisters said to her:

'You can wear some of our clothes; we have more than enough.'

'Thank you, dear sisters,' Maria said. 'But your clothes would not fit me. And I shall be quite happy at home.'

'Well, as you wish,' her father said. 'But what present shall I bring you back from the fair?'

'Oh, father, I do not need anything; I have all I want. It was not for nothing that I wore myself out on that long journey.'

So the father and the elder sisters drove off to the fair. As soon as they had gone Maria took out her feather, dropped it to the floor, and it changed into Finist, the handsome young man. But now he was even more handsome than before. Maria

was astonished, and in her happiness she could not say a word.

But he said to her:

'Do not be surprised, Maria; it is your love that has made me what I am.'

'I am astonished,' she said. 'But for me you are always the same; I love you however you look.'

'But where is your father?' he asked.

'He has driven to the fair with my elder sisters.'

'Then why did you not go with them?'

'I do not need anything at the fair. I have my Finist, my white falcon.'

'Nor do I need anything,' said Finist. 'And besides, through your love for me I have grown rich.'

He turned away, whistled at the window, and at once a golden carriage appeared, with rich attire. They dressed themselves in the fine clothing, got into the carriage, and the horses dashed off like the wind.

They drove to the fair in the town. But they went so fast that when they arrived the fair had only just begun; all the articles and food were lying in heaps, waiting for the customers who were still on their way to town. Finist bought everything there was for sale, including the food, and gave orders for it to be delivered to the house of Maria's father. The only thing he did not buy was cartwheel grease; he

left that because he wanted everybody who came to the fair to be guests at his wedding and to drive as fast as they could to the village. And in order to drive fast they would need the cartwheel grease.

Then Finist and Maria drove back to her home, so fast that the horses could hardly breathe. When they were halfway home Maria saw her father and sisters still driving on their way to the fair. She told them to turn back to the house, for her wedding with Finist the white falcon.

During the next three days all the people for sixty miles around arrived as guests for Maria's marriage to Finist, and the wedding was magnificent. The grandfathers and grandmothers were present, they feasted for days on end, and praised the bride and bridegroom. They would not have returned home until the oncoming of winter, but the harvesting season was at hand, the grain began to drop from the ear. And so the wedding festivities were brought to an end and the guests in time forgot the feast. But Maria's loving, faithful heart has been remembered for ever in the land of Russia.

Beautiful Vassilisa

MANY YEARS AGO, in a certain village lived an old couple, who had just one daughter, named Vassilisa. They lived in quite a small cottage, but they were comfortably off. Yet trouble came to them too, for the mother fell ill, and she realised that she was near to death. So she called her daughter to her, and gave her a small doll.

'Listen, my dear daughter,' she said. 'Take great care of this little doll, and never let anyone else see it. If you ever get into trouble, give her something to eat and ask her advice. She will eat the food and will help you in your trouble.'

She gave Vassilisa a last kiss, and soon after she died.

Although the old man mourned the loss of his wife, after some time he married again, thinking he would find his daughter a second mother. But all he gave her was an unkind stepmother. The new wife had two daughters of her own, who were stupid and fussy, and not at all good-natured. Their mother was very fond of them, but she made Vassilisa's life a misery. She was always scolding her, treating her unkindly, working her hard. And her daughters were just

as bad. They did their best to make her look thin by overworking her, and to spoil her good looks by exposing her to the sun and the wind. All day the girl heard nothing but: 'Get on with cooking the dinner, Vassilisa! It is time you swept out the home. Fetch some firewood, the fire is going out. Have you milked the cows yet? Do not stand there doing nothing, get a move on. You must work faster.'

Vassilisa was very willing, she did everything they asked, was always trying to please them, and managed the work very well. And with every day she grew more and more good-looking. She was too beautiful to be described. And she found the little doll of great help. Early every morning Vassilisa got some milk, shut herself away in the pantry, gave the doll the milk, and said to it:

'Drink up, Dollie, and listen to my troubles.'

The doll drank the milk and comforted the girl, and did all the work for her. Vassilisa would sit quietly somewhere in the shade, before anyone else was up, while the doll weeded the flower beds, fetched water, lit the stove, watered the cabbages. The doll even showed Vassilisa certain herbs that would protect her from sunburn, and so the girl grew more beautiful than ever.

Then a day came when her father had to be away from home for some time. It was late autumn, and it was dark outside the cottage; rain was falling, and the wind was howling. So the stepmother and her daughters would not set foot outside the house. All around the village was a deep forest, and in the forest lived the witch Baba Yaga: she ate people as if they were chicks.

The stepmother gave all the girls work to do; one of her daughters was to make lace, the second to knit stockings, while Vassilisa was to spin. She put out all the lights except one small glimmer where the girls were working, and then lay down to have a sleep. But the birch splinter which the girls were using for light crackled and spluttered, and at last went out.

'Now what are we to do?' the stepmother's daughters wondered. 'There is not a light anywhere in the house, and we have our work to do. Someone must go to the witch Baba Yaga and get light.'

'But I shall not go,' the elder stepdaughter said. 'I am knitting lace, and the crochet hook gives me all the light I need.'

'And I shall not go either,' the second stepdaughter said. 'I am knitting stockings, and the needles give me all the light I need.'

And they both cried at once:

'Then Vassilisa must go for the light. Go to the witch Baba Yaga, Vassilisa!' And they pushed the girl out of the house.

All around her Vassilisa saw only the dark night and the deep forest, she heard only the angry wind. She burst into tears, and took the doll out of her pocket.

'My darling Dollie,' she said, 'they are sending me to the witch Baba Yaga for light. And the witch eats people and crunches the bones.'

'Do not worry,' the doll told her. 'While I am with you nothing will happen to you. So long as you have me no harm will touch you.'

'Thank you, Dollie, for your kind words,' Vassilisa said, and she set out to go to the witch's hut. All around her the forest stood like a wall; she could not see any stars shining, and the bright moon did not rise. She walked along trembling, pressing the doll to her breast.

Suddenly a horseman galloped past her; he was dressed in white, he was riding a white horse, and the horse's harness was bright.

Dawn began to break.

As Vassilisa went on she stumbled, and hurt herself against a stump. Dew clung to her pigtail, her hands were icy with cold.

Suddenly a second horseman galloped past; he was dressed in red, was riding a red horse, and the horse's harness was red.

The sun rose. It caressed Vassilisa, warmed her, and dried the dew on her pigtail.

All day she walked on. Towards evening she came to a glade. She looked into the glade and saw a hut; all round it was a fence made from human bones. On the fence

were human skulls; human legbones served instead of a gate, there were hands instead of bolts, and sharp teeth acted as the lock.

At this sight the girl was terrified: she stood rooted to the ground. Suddenly a horseman rode past; he was dressed entirely in black, was riding a black horse, and the horse's harness, too, was black. He galloped up to the gate and vanished as if he had been swallowed into the earth.

Night came on.

And as darkness fell all the eyesockets of the skulls on the fence began to glow, and it grew as light as day in the glade. Vassilisa

trembled with fear. She could not move, her feet would not carry her away from the fearful spot.

Suddenly she heard and felt the earth quivering and shaking as though rocked by an earthquake. It was the witch on her way home; she was riding in a mortar, using a pestle to urge it on, and sweeping away her tracks with a besom. As she rode up to the gate she screamed:

'Pfooh! Pfooh! The place stinks of a Russian soul. Who is here?'

Vassilisa went up to her, bowed very low, and spoke very humbly:

'It is I, Grannie,' she said. 'My stepmother's daughters have sent me to you to get a light.'

'Ah, yes,' the witch said. 'Your step-mother's a relation of mine. Well, you can stay and work for me, and then we will see about the light.' Then she shouted: 'Hey, my powerful bolts, unfasten yourselves! My broad gates, open for me!'

The gates opened, and the witch rode in. Vassilisa followed her. By the gate a birch tree was growing; it tried to lash Vassilisa with its branches.

'Do not whip the girl, birch tree,' the witch said. 'I have brought her in.'

At the door a dog was lying; it tried to bite the girl.

'Do not touch her; I have brought her in,' said the witch.

In the porch a snarling cat tried to scratch the girl.

'Do not touch her, snarling cat, I have brought her in,' the witch said again.

She turned to Vassilisa: 'As you see,' she said, 'it is not easy to get away from me. The cat scratches, the dog bites, the birch will lash out your eyes, the gates will not open.' She went into the hut, stretched herself out on a bench, and called:

'Hey, swarthy child, get me some food.'

A swarthy young girl ran in and began to feed the witch; she brought a cauldron of beetroot soup, a bucket of milk, twenty young chicks, forty ducklings, and two pies, as well as endless quantities of kvass, mead, and beer. The witch ate and drank the lot. She gave Vassilisa only a crust of bread.

'Well, Vassilisa,' she said, 'now take this sack of millet and sort it out seed by seed. Take out all the black seed. And if you do not get it all done I will eat you.'

Then she lay down, and soon started to snore.

Vassilisa took the crust of bread, set it before the doll, and said:

'Dollie, Dollie, eat the bread and listen to my troubles. The witch has given me a difficult task, and she says she will eat me if I do not get it all done.'

But the doll replied:

'Do not cry. Better go and lie down to sleep. You will feel better after a good sleep.'

As soon as Vassilisa had dozed off the doll cried:

'Little birdies, tomtits, sparrows, and doves, fly here and save Vassilisa from harm.'

At once all sorts of birds came flying up

in great numbers. Trilling and cooing, they set to work to sort the millet, putting the good grain into a sack, and the black grains into their crops. They sorted out all the grain seed by seed, and cleansed it of all the weed seeds.

Just as the task was finished a white horseman on a white horse galloped past the gates. Dawn came.

The witch woke up, and at once asked Vassilisa:

'Well, have you done the work?'

'It is all done, Grannie,' she answered.

The witch flew into a rage, but there was nothing she could do.

'Well,' she grumbled, 'I have to fly off now to fetch something. But take that sack over there; in it peas are mixed with poppy seed. Sort them all out, seed by seed, and put them into two heaps. And if you do not get it done I will eat you.'

She went out and whistled, and the mortar and pestle rolled up to her door.

A red horseman galloped past. The sun rose.

The witch seated herself in the mortar and rode out of the yard, using the pestle as a stick, and sweeping away her tracks with a besom.

Vassilisa took a crust of bread, fed the doll, and said:

'Have pity on me, Dollie dear. Help me.'

The doll cried in a loud voice:

'Hurry to me, field mice, house mice, granary mice!'

The mice came running up in multitudes. And in an hour they had sorted all the peas from the poppy seed.

Late in the afternoon the swarthy child laid the table, and waited for the witch to return. A black horseman galloped past the gate. Night fell. In the skulls the eye sockets began to burn, the trees creaked, the leaves rustled. Baba Yaga, the bony-legged witch, was on her way home.

'Well, how about it, Vassilisa?' she asked as soon as she came in. 'Done all the work?'

'It is all done, Grannie,' the girl answered.

The witch was furious, but she could do nothing.

'In that case,' she said, 'go to bed, and I will lie down in a moment.'

Vassilisa went to lie down behind the stove. But before she could get to sleep she heard the witch say:

'Swarthy girl, make the stove really hot, get a blazing fire going. When I wake up I am going to cook Vassilisa.'

Then she stretched herself out on a bench, covered her feet, and started to snore so loudly that she could have been heard all through the forest.

Vassilisa lay in her corner, weeping. But then she took out her doll and set a crust of bread before it. 'My darling Dollie,' she said. 'Eat the bread and listen to my troubles.' The doll ate the bread, and then told Vassilisa all she had to do in order to escape from the witch. So the girl went to the swarthy child, and bowed to her.

'Help me, swarthy child,' she pleaded. 'Do not burn the wood, but make it only smoulder by wetting it with water. Here, take my silk handkerchief as a present.'

'All right,' the girl said, 'I will help you. I will take a long time over lighting the stove, and tickle Baba Yaga's feet to make her sleep more soundly. And you run away home, darling Vassilisa.'

'But do you think one of the horsemen will catch me?' Vassilisa asked anxiously. 'Will they come back?'

'Oh no,' the girl answered. 'The white horseman is the broad daylight, the red horseman is the golden sun, and the black horseman is the dark night. They will not hurt you.'

Vassilisa ran out into the porch. The snarling cat rushed at her and tried to scratch her. But she threw it a patty, and it did not touch her. She ran down the steps. The dog jumped up and tried to bite her. But she threw him some bread. And the dog let her pass. She ran through the yard. The birch tree tried to lash her eyes out. But she tied it with a ribbon, and the birch let her pass. The gates wanted to swing shut against her. But she greased their hinges

with grease, and they opened for her.

But now the black horseman galloped past; in the forest it grew darker than dark. How could she ever find her way home without a light? Her stepmother would beat the life out of her if she returned without it. But once more the doll instructed her what to do. She took a skull off the fence, and set it on a pole. Then she ran through the deep forest, and the eyesockets in the skull shone so brightly that the dark night was lit up like day.

After a nap the old witch woke up and stretched herself. She went to catch Vassilisa to cook her, and ran into the porch.

'Snarling cat,' she said. 'The girl ran past you. Why did you not scratch her?'

But the snarling cat answered:

'I have served you for ten years, Baba Yaga, and you have never even given me a crust. But she gave me a patty, so I let her pass.'

Then the witch rushed into the yard and cried:

'My faithful hound, why did you not bite the disobedient girl?'

But the dog answered:

'I have served you all these years, and you have never even thrown me a bone. But she gave me bread, so I let her pass.'

The witch screamed hoarsely:

'Birch tree, my birch tree, why did you not lash out her eyes?'

But the birch tree answered:

'I have been growing in your yard for ten years, and you never tied up my branches even with string. But she bound me with ribbon, so I let her pass.'

The witch ran to the gates:

'My powerful gates, why did you not close and shut in the disobedient girl?'

But the gates answered her:

'We have served you so long, and you never even poured water on our hinges.

But she greased them with grease, so we let her pass.'

The witch was furious, and she started beating the dog, shaking the cat, chopping down the birch, breaking down the gate. But she did not try to go after Vassilisa to catch her.

Meanwhile Vassilisa ran all the way home. When she arrived she saw there was still no light in the house. Her stepsisters ran out and swore at her, reproaching her.

'Why have you been so long bringing the light?' they demanded. 'We simply cannot keep any light going in the house. We have struck and struck the flint against the iron, but it never gave a spark to set the tinder alight. We hope the light you have brought will stay alight.'

They carried the skull into the best room, and there the skull's eyesockets glared at the stepmother and her daughters so fiercely that they were burnt with fire. They tried to hide from the skull, but wherever they ran the glare of the eyesockets followed them and found them. By the morning they were burnt into cinders.

But the fire did not harm Vassilisa. In the morning she took the skull and buried it in the ground, and a crimson rose bush sprang up in the spot where she buried it.

She did not feel that she wanted to remain in the house alone, so she went to the town and began to live with an old woman. One day she said to the old woman:

'Grannie, I am bored with sitting here doing nothing. Buy me some flax, the very finest you can get.'

The old woman bought the flax, and Vassilisa sat down to spin it. The work flew so fast in her hands that the spindle hummed. The thread came away even and fine, like a golden hair. Then she set to work to weave the thread, and she wove linen that could have been passed through a needle eye just like a thread. Then she bleached the linen whiter than snow.

'Now, Grannie,' she said, 'go and sell the linen and keep whatever you get for it.'

The old woman gasped at the linen:

'No, I shall not sell it,' she said. 'It is too good. Only a prince should wear such linen. I will take it to the prince.'

When the prince saw the linen he was astonished at its quality. 'What do you want for it?' he asked.

'Such linen is without price,' the old woman answered. 'So I have brought it to you as a gift.'

The prince thanked her and sent her home with presents. The servants wanted to make a shirt for him from the linen, but when they saw it no one would undertake the task: it was too fine for them to handle. So the prince sent for the old woman and said:

'As you have been clever enough to weave such fine linen, now make me a shirt from it.'

'It was not I who span and wove it, prince,' the old woman answered. 'It was the girl Vassilisa.'

'Well then, let her make the shirt,' he told her.

The old woman went back home and told Vassilisa what the prince had said. The girl made the shirt, trimmed it with silks, and decorated it with seed pearls. Then the old woman carried it back to the palace.

Vassilisa sat down at the cottage window to do some embroidering on a tambour. Suddenly she saw one of the prince's servants come running along the street. He hurried up to her window, and told her:

'The prince requires you to go to the palace.'

So she went to the palace. And when the prince saw how beautiful she was he stood rooted to the spot.

'I do not intend to let you go away,' he said. 'I want you to be my wife.'

He took her white hands, seated her at his side, and there and then they celebrated the wedding. Soon after they had got married Vassilisa's father returned from his travels, and he went to live in the palace with his daughter. Vassilisa took the old woman who had helped her into her service. And she always carried the doll in her pocket. Vassilisa and the prince were very happy.

The Golden Fish

THERE ARE MANY ISLANDS in the sea, and not all of them are inhabited. But on one island, at one time, there was a small, tumbledown cottage which belonged to an old man and his wife. They were very poor, and the husband used to make nets and fish in the sea, for that was the only food they could get. One day he went fishing as usual; he cast his net, and started to draw it in, for it seemed heavier that it had ever been before. He only just managed to draw it up. Yet when he looked he found the net was empty except for one small fish. However, it was no ordinary fish, for it was golden. Even stranger, it pleaded with the old man, speaking in a human voice: 'Do not kill me; put me back into the blue sea. I can be of some service to you: whatever you wish, I will do.'

The old man thought it over, and answered: 'I do not need anything from you; go back and swim in the sea.' He threw the fish back into the water and went off home. But when he got home his wife asked him: 'Did you catch many fish, old man?' So he told her: 'Only one little golden fish, and it pleaded so hard for its life that I threw it

back into the sea. It did say it would be of service to me, and do whatever I wished.'

'Ah, you old fool,' said his wife; 'you had a great fortune in your hands, and you did not know what to do with it.' She was furious at what he had done, nagged him all day, and gave him no peace. 'You could at least have asked it for some bread,' she said. 'Before long we will not even have any dry crusts, and then what will you eat?' She went on nagging him till at last he could stand no more, and he went to the sea to ask the golden fish for some bread.

When he reached the seashore he shouted in a loud voice: 'Little fish, little fish; stand up with your tail in the sea and your head turned towards me.' The fish swam up to the shore, and asked: 'What do you want, old man?'

'My old woman's very angry, she sent me to ask you for bread,' he said. 'Go home again,' said the fish; 'you will find plenty of bread there.' The old man went back home and asked his wife: 'Well, is there any bread now?'

'We have got bread in plenty,' she told him, 'but now we are in trouble; the wooden washing bath has split, and I have nothing to wash the clothes in. Go back to the golden fish and ask it to give us a new one.'

So the old man went to the seashore and called: 'Little fish, little fish, stand up with your tail in the sea, your head turned towards me.' The little golden fish swam up and asked: 'What do you want, old man?'

'My wife has sent me to ask for a new wooden washing bath,' he told it. 'Good! You shall have the bath too,' the fish assured him. So he went back home. But he had got no farther than the door when his wife came rushing at him: 'Go to the golden fish,' she said, 'and ask it to build us a new cottage. This one is quite impossible to live in, it could fall to pieces any moment.'

The old man went down to the seashore and called: 'Little fish, little fish, stand up with your tail in the sea, your head turned towards me.' The fish swam up, stood with its tail in the sea and its head turned towards him, and asked: 'What do you want, old man?'

'Build us a new cottage,' he asked the fish. 'My old wife is discontented, she will not give me any peace. "I do not want to live in that old hut," she says, "it could fall to pieces any moment."'

'Do not worry, old man. Go back home and pray to God; it will all be done,' said the fish. The old man returned home, and found a new cottage built of oaken logs, with fretwork ornamentation along the eaves. His old wife came running out to meet him, angrier than ever, swearing at him more than ever. 'Ah, you old fool, you do not know how to take advantage of your good fortune,' she exclaimed. 'You ask for a new cottage, and you think it ends there. But it does not. Go back to the golden fish and tell it your wife does not want to be a peasant woman; she wants to be a woman governor, she wants the people to obey her, and to bow low when they meet her.'

So the old man went down to the seashore, and called in a loud voice: 'Little fish, little fish, stand up with your tail in the sea, your head towards me.' The fish swam up, stood with its head turned towards him and its tail in the sea, and asked: 'What do

you want, old man?' He answered: 'My old woman gives me no peace; she is quite mad. She does not want to be a peasant woman any more, she wants to be a woman governor.'

'Good! Do not worry,' said the fish. 'Go back home and pray to God; it will be done.' When the old man returned home he saw that instead of his new cottage he now had a house built of bricks, three storeys high. Servants were running about the courtyard, cooks were bustling in the kitchen. And his old woman, wearing an expensive brocade gown, was sitting on a high chair and giving orders. 'Hello, wife,' the old man said.

'How dare you call me, a governor, your wife!' she stormed. 'Hey, men, take this funny old fellow into the stables and give him a good whipping.' Servants ran up, seized the old man by the collar, and dragged him to the stable. There the stable-boys treated him to such a sound whipping, that afterwards he could hardly stand. Then his old wife made him a yardsman; she ordered him to be given a broom to sweep the yard, and he was to have his meals in the kitchen.

Now the poor old man had a bad time; he spent all day sweeping the yard, and as soon as the least speck of dirt was noticed which he had left he was hauled off to the stable for a beating. 'What an old witch she is!' he thought. 'She has been given all this good fortune and she is wallowing in it like a pig. She does not even regard me as her husband any longer.'

As time passed the old woman grew bored with being a governor, so she sent for the old man and told him: 'You old fool, go to the golden fish and tell it I do not want to be a governor any more. I want to be the queen.'

So the old man wandered down to the seashore and called: 'Little fish, little fish! Stand up with your tail in the sea, your head turned towards me.' The little golden fish swam up and asked: 'What do you want, old man?'

'What do I want!' he answered. 'It is not me, it is my old woman; she is crazier than ever; now she does not want to be a governor any more, she wants to be a queen.'

'Do not worry,' said the fish. 'Go home

and pray to God; it will be done.' When the old man returned, in place of the former house, he now saw a lofty palace with a golden roof; all around it sentries were marching to and fro and exercising with their guns; on a great meadow in front of it, soldiers were drawn up. He found his old woman dressed as a queen. But after some time the old woman grew bored with being a queen, so she ordered the old man to be found and brought before her regal eyes.

That really did cause a to-do, for no one knew anything about the old man. The generals fussed about, the courtiers ran back and forth, asking: 'Who or what is this old man she is asking for?' But at last they found him in the backyard, and led him before the queen. 'You old fool,' his wife said to him, 'go to the little golden fish and tell it I do not want to be a queen any more. I want to be empress of all the seas, I want all the seas and all the fishes to obey me.' At first the old man refused to go. But she told him: 'If you do not go I will have your head off.' Grinding his teeth, he went to the seashore and called:

'Little fish, little fish, stand up with your tail in the sea, your head turned towards me.' But the little golden fish did not appear. He called a second time, but still it did not come. When he called a third time, suddenly the sea began to roar and to rise in great waves. The day had been bright and clear, but now it turned quite dark. Then the golden fish swam up to the shore and asked: 'What do you want, old man?' He answered: 'My old woman's completely mad; she no longer wants to be queen, she wants to be empress of all the seas, to rule over all the waters, and to have all the fishes obey her.' The little golden fish made no answer to the old man; it simply turned tail and swam off into the depths of the sea.

So the old man had to return home. But when he got there he stood looking and staring, unable to believe his eyes: the palace had vanished as though it had never been, and in its place was his old, small, tumbledown hut, and inside it his wife was sitting in a ragged dress. They began to live their former life, and he went fishing. But no matter how often he cast his net into the sea he never again managed to catch the little golden fish.

Marko the Wealthy
and Vassily the Luckless

ONCE UPON A TIME, in a certain kingdom, there was a merchant named Marko who was so rich that the people gave him the nickname 'the Wealthy'. He possessed incalculable treasure, but he was miserly and never gave anything to the poor. He disliked beggars, and if he happened to see one around he ordered his servants to drive him out of the yard and set the dogs on him.

Late one evening two grey-haired old men came to him as he was standing in his yard, and pleaded: 'Marko the Wealthy, for pity's sake give us shelter against the dark night.' They pleaded so long and so persistently that, in order to get rid of them, Marko gave orders that they could stay in the cattle shed, where his ailing old aunt was lying on the point of death. Next day Marko saw his aunt coming towards him across the yard perfectly well. 'How did you manage it?' he asked in amazement. 'Ah, Marko the Wealthy', his aunt answered, 'do you know what? I do not know whether I was dreaming, but last night I thought I saw two old men with us in the cattle shed. At the very hour of midnight someone knocked at the window and asked them: "In such and such a village a child has been born to a poor peasant; what name do you give him and what gift do you assign to him?" The old men answered: "We name him Vassily; his nickname is to be 'the Luckless', and we assign him as his gift all the riches of Marko the Wealthy, with whom we are spending this night".' 'And what else happened?' Marko asked. 'Why, what a blessing I had! When I woke up I was able to stand up perfectly well, as you see.' 'That is fine!' said Marko. 'But I do not see that poor peasant's son possessing a lot of my wealth. Not if I know it!'

However, when he had considered it carefully he thought he would like to find out whether a baby named Vassily, and nicknamed 'the Luckless', really had been born in that village. So he ordered his carriage to be brought to the door, and drove to the village priest. He asked him: 'Was a male child born here a few days ago?' 'Yes,' the priest replied. 'It was born to the poorest peasant in the village. I named it Vassily and gave it the nickname "the Luckless". But I have not christened him

yet, because no one wants to act as god-
parent to the poor wretch.' Then Marko
offered to be the godfather, asked the
priest's wife to be the godmother, and gave
orders for a splendid dinner to be prepared.
The young child was christened, and they
feasted till late in the night. Next day
Marko the Wealthy sent for the child's
father, talked to him kindly, and said:
'Cousin, you are a poor man; you cannot
bring up your son, so let me have him. I
will see he makes his way in the world, and

give you a thousand roubles to live on.' After thinking it over the peasant agreed. Marko took the baby, wrapped it in a greatcoat of fox fur, put it in his carriage and drove away. It happened to be winter time. After driving several miles Marko ordered his coachman to stop, gave his god-child to his steward, and told him: 'Take it by the legs and throw it into a ravine.' The steward took the child and threw it into a deep ravine; and Marko grinned as he said: 'You can take over all my property down there!'

Two days later some merchants happened to be driving along the same road; they were taking Marko twelve thousand roubles which they owed him. When they drew level with the ravine they heard a child crying. They stopped and listened, and one of them sent his servant to find out what it was all about. The servant climbed down to the bottom of the ravine, and came to a green glade; in the glade a child was sitting, surrounded by flowers. The servant climbed back and told his master what he had seen, and the merchant himself hurried down to see this marvellous sight. He picked up the child, wrapped it in a great-coat, got into his carriage, and drove on. When the merchants reached Marko's house he asked them where they had found the child. The merchants told him what had happened, and he guessed at once that the child was Vassily the Luckless, his own godson. He entertained the merchants hospitably, and then asked them to let him have their foundling. At first they were rather reluctant to agree, but when he told them that he would release them from all their debts to him they handed over the little child. Three days later Marko took Vassily the Luckless, put him into a barrel, tarred the barrel and threw it off the jetty into the river.

The barrel floated down the river until it reached a monastery. Just as it was passing the monastery a monk came out to fetch water from the river. He heard a child crying, and without waiting a moment he got into a boat, rowed up to the barrel, knocked away the hoops, saw a child inside, took it out and carried it to the monastery. The Father Superior called the child Vassily and nicknamed him the 'Luckless'. And Vassily the Luckless lived in the mona-stery a full eighteen years. He learned his letters, could read and write, and sang in the choir. The Father Superior grew very fond of him and made him the sacristan.

Eighteen years after he had thrown the child into the river, Marko the Wealthy had to travel to another country to collect some debts, and on the way he turned aside into the monastery. He noticed a young sacristan there, and inquired whether he had been in the monastery for any length of time. The Father Superior told him how the young sacristan had been found as a baby in a barrel in the river, and how many years ago it had happened. Marko reckoned it out and realised that the sacristan was no other than his godson. So he said to the Father Superior: 'If I had such an efficient fellow as your sacristan working for me I would make him my chief steward. Let me have him.' At first the Father Superior was very reluctant to part with Vassily.

But when at last Marko the Wealthy offered to make a contribution of twenty-five thousand roubles to the monastery the Father Superior discussed it with the other brothers, and they eventually agreed to accept this in exchange for Vassily.

Marko ordered Vassily to make his way back to Marko's home, and gave him a letter to give to his wife. It read: 'Wife! As soon as you get this letter go with the bearer to our soap works and order the workers there to push him into the great cauldron of boiling fat. Be sure to do as I tell you: this lad stole from me some time ago.' As Vassily was travelling back to Marko's house he fell in with an old, grey-headed man, who asked him: 'Where are you going, Vassily the Luckless?' 'I am going to Marko the

Wealthy's house,' he answered. 'My master has sent me back with a letter.' 'Let me see the letter,' the old man asked. Vassily gave him the letter, he broke the seal, and said: 'Here, read it!' Vassily read it, and burst into tears. 'What have I done to this man?' he exclaimed. 'Why does he want to condemn me to a cruel death?' 'Do not grieve, or be afraid,' the old man reassured him. 'The Lord will not desert you.' He blew on the letter, and the seal was made whole again. 'Now go with God and hand the letter to Marko's wife,' he instructed Vassily. So Vassily went on, arrived at Marko's house, asked for the mistress, and gave her the letter. When she had read it she summoned her daughter, Anastasia, and showed her what her father had written. The letter now read: 'Wife! When you receive this letter, the very next day marry Anastasia to the bearer. Be sure to carry out this order faithfully.'

People with lots of money do not have to make their own beer or press their own wine, and everything was to hand for a merry feast. Vassily was provided with new clothes, and then Anastasia was brought in for him to see his future wife. He fell in love with her at once, and the couple were driven to church, where the priest married them.

One morning some time later Marko's wife was informed that her husband had arrived at the jetty, and she went with her daughter and son-in-law to meet him. When Marko the Wealthy saw Vassily the Luckless he flew into a rage and shouted at his wife. 'How did you dare to marry our daughter to him?' 'It was on your orders,' his wife answered. So Marko asked to see the letter she had received, read it, and could not deny that it was all in his own handwriting.

Some three months passed. Then Marko the Wealthy sent for his son-in-law and told

him: 'You are to travel through twenty-seven lands to the thirtieth country, where the Tsar Serpent rules. Collect twelve years' tribute from him, and while you are there find out what has happened to twelve ships of mine, which have been missing for three years. And set off tomorrow at dawn.'

Early next morning Vassily the Luckless got up, prayed to God, said goodbye to his wife, filled a bag with rusks and set off on his journey.

When he had been travelling for some time he heard a voice coming from the side of the road. 'Vassily the Luckless, where are you going?' it asked.

'To the Tsar Serpent,' he answered, 'to collect twelve years' tribute. But who wants to know?'

'I, the oak, am asking you.' Vassily looked in the direction of the voice, and saw an old oak standing at the wayside. And the tree went on: 'While you are with the Tsar

Serpent, make mention of me. Tell him that I, the oak, have been standing here for three hundred years, and ask him whether I have to go on standing for much longer.' Vassily the Luckless listened to the oak's request, and then went on his way. After walking for some time he came to a great, wide river, where he had to take the ferry. As they were crossing the river the ferryman asked him where he was going. Vassily answered: 'I am going to the Tsar Serpent to demand payment of twelve years' tribute.'

'While you are there,' said the ferryman, 'make mention of me. Tell him I have been ferrying here for exactly thirty years, and ask him if I have to go on ferrying people for much longer.'

'Good!' Vassily said, and went on his way. After many days he came to the blue sea. There he saw a whale stretching right across the sea, and people on foot and on horseback were crossing it as if it were a bridge. The moment Vassily set foot on the whale it spoke to him, asking: 'Where are you going, Vassily the Luckless?' 'I am going to the Tsar Serpent to collect twelve years' tribute,' Vassily told it. 'Well, my good man, while you are there make mention of me. Tell him I have been lying right across the blue sea for a long time; people

crossing on foot and on horseback have worn my body down right to the ribs. Have I got to go on lying here much longer, being used as a bridge?'

'Good, I shall not forget,' Vassily assured the whale, and went on.

At last he came to a green meadow; in the middle of it was a large palace. Vassily went up the steps, and passed through room after room, through carved, decorated doorways. Each room as he came to it was better furnished than the last; in the very farthest room a beautiful girl was sitting on a bed. When she saw him enter she went up to him and asked: 'Who are you, young man? How did you get to this accursed spot?'

'My name is Vassily the Luckless,' he told her, 'and I have been sent by Marko the Wealthy to find Tsar Serpent and extract twelve years' tribute from him.'

'Ah, Vassily the Luckless,' she answered, 'you have been sent here not to collect tribute, but to be food for the Tsar Serpent. Which way did you come? Did you happen to see or hear anything on the road, young man?'

So he told her about the ancient oak, the ferryman, and the whale. They had not had time to talk long when a whirlwind began to howl, the earth shook, and the palace swayed: the Tsar Serpent was coming. The

beautiful girl hid Vassily under the bed and told him: 'Lie there and listen carefully to what I say to the Serpent, and what he answers.'

The Tsar Serpent flew into the room. 'What is this smell of a Russian soul hanging about here?' he demanded to know. 'How could a Russian soul ever get here?' the beautiful girl answered. 'You must have been flying over Russia and the smell of Russian souls must have clung to you.' 'Well, I am very tired,' he said. 'I will lie down and you can search my head for fleas.' And he stretched himself out on the bed. The girl started to look for fleas in his head. While she was looking she said: 'Tsar, while you have been away I have had a strange dream. I seemed to be going along a road, and an old oak called to me: "ask the tsar whether I have to go on standing here much longer?"' 'It will have to go on standing,' the Serpent answered, 'until a fine young man comes along and kicks it with his foot at sunrise. Then the oak will be overthrown by the roots, and under it the young man will find gold and silver in large quantities, even more than Marko the Wealthy possesses.' 'And then I dreamed,' the girl went on, 'that I came to a wide river where there is a ferry, and the ferryman asked me whether he had to go on much

longer sitting in his boat and ferrying people across.' 'No, it will not be long now,' the Tsar Serpent answered. 'He must seat the first man who turns up in his place and push the ferry away from the bank. Then the other man will have to take

his place as the permanent ferryman.' 'And then I dreamed that I was walking over a whale,' the girl continued. 'I was crossing the blue sea on the whale, and it asked me whether it had to lie there acting as a bridge for much longer.' 'It will lie there,' the Tsar Serpent declared, 'until it spews out of its stomach the twelve vessels belonging to Marko the Wealthy. When it spews out these ships it will swim off into the sea, and its bones will be clothed with flesh, and its body made whole.' And then the Serpent went off into a deep sleep.

The beautiful girl drew Vassily the Luckless out from under the bed, and gave him the advice: 'When you go back, do not tell the whale or the ferryman what you have just heard from the Tsar Serpent until you get to the other side. Then you will arrive safely home.' Vassily the Luckless thanked her, and set off on his road back. When he came again to the blue sea the whale asked him: 'Well, did you mention me to the Tsar Sepent?' 'Yes,' Vassily

answered, 'but I will tell you what he said when I get to the other side.' He walked on the whale across the sea to the other shore, and then said: 'Spew out of your stomach the twelve ships that belong to Marko the Wealthy.' The whale belched and the twelve ships came out of its mouth, with their sails set and quite unharmed. But the waves rolled so high up the shore as the whale moved off that Vassily found himself in water up to his knees, though he ran back quite a distance.

When he came to the ferry the ferryman asked him:

'Did you speak to the Tsar Serpent about me?' 'Yes, I did,' Vassily answered. 'Well, and what did he say?' 'You ferry me across to the other bank, and then I will tell you,'

Vassily answered. So they crossed to the farther bank, and he told the ferryman: 'Seat the first man who comes along in your place, push the ferry off from the bank, and go home.' Finally he came to the ancient oak, and at dawn the next morning he kicked it with his foot. The oak crashed down, tearing up its roots, and beneath it he found gold and silver, and precious stones innumerable. He looked back, and saw twelve ships, the same ships that the whale had spewed out, come sailing right up to the bank. The sailors carried the gold and silver and precious stones on board, and set sail again, taking Vassily with them.

A servant brought Marko the Wealthy the news that his son-in-law was sailing home with the twelve ships, and that the Tsar Serpent had bestowed incalculable wealth on Vassily. Marko was furious at these tidings; he ordered horses to be harnessed to his carriage at once, and drove off to the Tsar Serpent to find out how he could rid himself of his son-in-law. He drove up to the ferry and the ferryman seated him in his place, pushed the ferry away from the bank, and went home. And from then on Marko the Wealthy had to spend his days ferrying people across the river.

But Vassily the Luckless arrived safely home to his wife and mother-in-law, and began to live very happily. He accumulated wealth, he helped the poor, and the orphans. And, as had been foretold, he had charge of all Marko the Wealthy's possessions.

As the Pike Orders

ONCE UPON A TIME there was a farmer who had three sons, who lived with him on the farm. The two elder brothers were intelligent; they had married sensible wives and they worked hard. But the third brother, Emelian, was slow-witted, and he spent all day lying by the stove. He never wanted to do anything!

One day his brothers drove to market, and while they were gone their wives thought it would be a good idea to make Emelian do some work. So they told him:

'Emelian, go and fetch us some water from the river.'

He made no attempt to move, but lay on the stove and answered:

'I do not want to.'

'Go and fetch it, Emelian,' the two wives scolded, 'or your brothers will not bring you any sweets back from market.'

'Oh, all right,' he grumbled. He slipped down from the stove, dressed, picked up two buckets and went off to the river. There he broke a hole in the ice, filled the buckets with water, and set them down, while he gazed into the hole. He had seen a pike in the hole, and somehow he managed to catch the fish with his hands. For he was thinking:

'Its roe will make a tasty supper.'

But the pike started talking to him in a human voice:

'Emelian,' it said, 'put me back into the water, I will do you a service.'

'What service can you do me?' Emelian said with a laugh. 'Not me! I will carry you

home and tell the women to cook your roe. We will have a tasty supper.'

But the pike pleaded:

'Emelian, Emelian, put me back in the water; I will do all you wish.'

'All right,' said Emelian, 'but first show that you are not tricking me, then I will let you go.'

So the pike asked him:

'Emelian, Emelian, tell me what you you would like at this very moment.'

'I would like the buckets to take themselves home without spilling any water,' he said.

Then the pike told him:

'Remember what I am saying: whenever you want something, all you need say is:

"As the pike orders,
And as I desire . . ." '

So Emelian said:

'As the pike orders,
And as I desire . . .

'Buckets, take yourselves home!'

And as soon as he said the words the buckets set off up the hill, all on their own. So he put the pike back into the hole, and went off after the buckets.

They went right through the village, and the people were astonished at the sight. But Emelian walked along behind the buckets, laughing. They went into the hut and put themselves on a bench, and then he went back to the stove.

Some time later the women said to him:

'Emelian, what are you lying up there for? Why not go and chop some wood?'

'I do not want to,' said Emelian.

'If you do not chop some wood your brothers will not bring you any sweets back from the market,' they told him.

So he reluctantly left the stove. Then he remembered the pike, and said very quietly:

'As the pike orders,
And as I desire . . .

'Axe, go and chop the wood; and wood, go into the kitchen and feed the stove!'

The axe jumped out from under the bench, hopped into the yard, and began chopping wood. And the chopped wood

went into the hut and into the stove.

A few days later the women said again:

'Emelian, we have no more wood for chopping. Drive into the forest and cut down a tree.'

But he answered from the top of the stove:

'Why not go yourself?'

'What do you mean: is it our job to drive into the forest for wood?' they retorted.

'But I do not want to.'

'Well, your brothers will not bring you back any presents, then.'

There was nothing else for it! He slipped off the stove, put on his boots, and dressed. He picked up the axe and a rope, went into the yard and got into the sledge. Then he called to the women:

'Women, open the yard gates.'

But they answered:

'You fool, why have you got into the sledge, when you have not harnessed up the horses?'

'I do not need any horses,' he answered.

So the women opened the gates, and Emelian said very quietly:

> 'As the pike orders,
> And as I desire . . .

'Sledge, drive to the forest!'

The sledge drove off through the gates of itself, and it travelled so fast that no horses could ever have kept up with it.

But in order to reach the forest he had to pass through the town, and there the sledge drove over and crushed quite a lot of people. Everybody shouted after him: 'Hold him! Seize him!' But he only urged the sledge to go faster. When he reached the forest he said:

> 'As the pike orders,
> And as I desire . . .

'Axe, chop up some dry wood; and wood, pile yourself on the sledge, and tie yourself fast with the rope!'

The axe began chopping up the dry wood, and the pieces of wood as they were chopped piled themselves on the sledge, and ended by tying themselves firmly to the sledge with the rope. Then he ordered the axe to cut him a cudgel, one so big and heavy that he could hardly lift it. He seated himself on top of the wood, and said:

> 'As the pike orders,
> And as I desire . . .

'Sledge, drive home!'

And the sledge dashed off home. He had to pass again through the town where he had ridden over and crushed some people, and he found people waiting for him there. They seized him and dragged him off the sledge, swearing at him and beating him. He realised that matters were going badly for him, so he said very quietly:

> 'As the pike orders,
> And as I desire . . .

'Cudgel, beat them up!'

The cudgel jumped off the sledge and began to thrash around. The people fled in all directions, and Emelian climbed back on the sledge and rode home.

Of course, it was not long before the tsar heard of Emelian's little tricks, and he sent an officer to find him and bring him to the palace. The officer drove to Emelian's village, entered the hut, and asked him:

'Are you Emelian the fool?'

Emelian answered from the top of the stove:

'Well, what do you want?'

'Get dressed at once; I am taking you to the tsar,' the officer told him.

'But I do not want to go!'

The officer became very angry and struck him on the face. So Emelian said very quietly so that no one could hear:

> 'As the pike orders,
> And as I desire . . .

'Cudgel, give him a good hiding!'

The cudgel jumped up and thrashed the officer till he fled for his life.

The tsar was amazed to hear that his officer had not been able to deal with Emelian, and he turned to his chamberlain and told him:

'Bring Emelian the fool to me here in the palace, or I will have your head off.'

The chamberlain went to the market and bought raisins, sugar-plums, and gingerbreads. Then he drove to Emelian's village, entered the hut, and asked the women what Emelian was fond of.

'Our Emelian likes people to speak nicely to him, and to offer him a crimson tunic with a girdle. Then he will do whatever you want.'

The chamberlain gave Emelian the raisins, sugar-plums, and gingerbreads, and said:

'Emelian, Emelian, why are you lying by the stove? Let us drive to the tsar.'

'I'm just as warm here,' answered Emelian.

'Emelian, Emelian, the tsar will give you lots to eat and drink; please come.'

'But I do not want to go!'

'Emelian, Emelian, the tsar will give you a crimson tunic, cap, and boots,' the chamberlain promised.

Emelian thought it over and said at last:

'All right, I will come. You go on, and I will follow right behind.'

The chamberlain set off to drive back to the palace; but Emelian remained lying on the stove, and only said:

'As the pike orders,
   And as I desire . . .

'Now, stove, off you go to the tsar!'

The moment he had spoken the hut began to crack at the corners, the roof shivered and shook, one wall flew right out, and the stove went travelling of itself down the street, along the highroad, straight to the tsar, with Emelian on top of it.

The tsar looked out of his window and saw the stove coming. He was astonished, and asked:

'What is this marvel coming along?'

The chamberlain answered:

'It is Emelian riding to you on his stove.'

So the tsar went to the front door and spoke to Emelian:

'Look here, you Emelian,' he said, 'we have had a lot of complaints about you. You crushed a lot of people.'

'All right, but why did they want to crawl under the sledge?' Emelian answered.

Just then the tsar's daughter, Princess Maria, looked out of the window to see what was happening. Emelian saw her at the window and said very quietly:

'As the pike orders,
   And as I desire . . .

'Make the tsar's daughter fall in love with me!'

Then he added:

'Stove, take me home again.'

The stove turned round and went back, entered the hut, and stood in its former place. Emelian lay down, and went on lying on the stove.

But the tsar's palace was filled with the sound of weeping and crying. Princess Maria had such a terrible longing for Emelian that she swore she could not live without him. And she asked the tsar to let her marry him. The tsar was annoyed at the very idea, and he told his chamberlain:

'Go and bring Emelian to me alive or dead, or I will have your head off.'

The chamberlain bought sweet wines and all sorts of good things to eat, drove to the village, entered the hut and entertained Emelian with the food and drink. Emelian ate and drank so much that he became a little tipsy and lay down to sleep it off. Then the chamberlain put him in his carriage and carried him to the tsar.

The tsar gave orders for a great barrel with iron hoops to be brought, and told his men to put Emelian and Princess Maria into it. They tarred the barrel and rolled it into the sea.

When Emelian woke up he saw that he was in a dark and confined sort of prison.

'Where am I?' he asked.

And someone very close to him answered:

'It is boring and stifling in here, dearest Emelian. They've put us into a barrel and thrown it into the blue sea.'

'But who are you?' he wanted to know.

'I am Princess Maria,' she answered.

However, Emelian soon recovered from his alarm at being in the barrel, and said:

> 'As the pike orders,
> And as I desire . . .

'Stormy winds, blow this barrel to dry land, on to a yellow sandy shore.'

At once stormy winds began blowing and

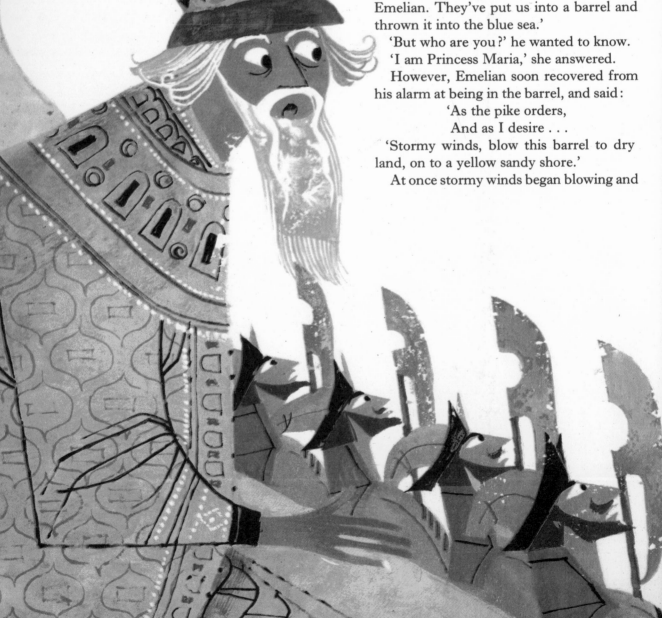

howling, the sea grew very rough, and it rolled the barrel on to the dry land, on to the yellow sand. Emelian and the princess climbed out of it.

'That is fine, dearest Emelian,' said the princess. 'But where are we going to live? Build a little hut of some sort.'

'But I do not want to,' said Emelian.

She started to nag at him to do something about it, so he said:

> 'As the pike orders,
> And as I desire . . .

'Build us a stone palace with a golden roof!'

He had no sooner spoken than a stone palace with a golden roof arose. It was surrounded by a green garden, in which flowers were blooming and birds singing. Princess Maria and Emelian entered the palace and sat down at a window. And the princess said to him:

'Emelian, dearest, would it be possible for you to turn yourself into a handsome young man?'

Emelian did not think long over that one. He said at once:

> 'As the pike orders,
> And as I desire . . .

'Change me into a handsome young man, as fine as a picture.'

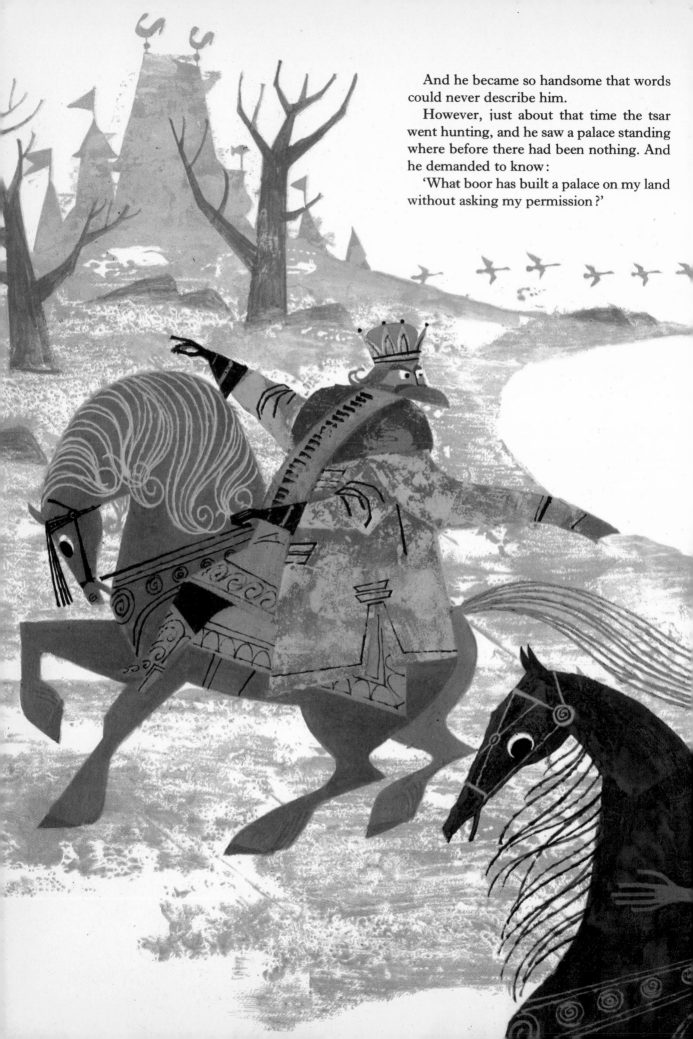

And he became so handsome that words could never describe him.

However, just about that time the tsar went hunting, and he saw a palace standing where before there had been nothing. And he demanded to know:

'What boor has built a palace on my land without asking my permission?'

And he sent to find out who was living in the palace. The messengers ran and stood under the window to make their inquiries. Emelian told them:

'Invite the tsar to come and be our guest, and I will tell him myself.'

So the tsar rode up to the palace to be the guest of his daughter and Emelian. Emelian met him, escorted him into the palace, seated him at the table, and they began to feast. The tsar ate and drank, and could not suppress his astonishment. He demanded:

'But who are you, my fine young man!'

Emelian told him:

'Do you remember Emelian the fool, who rode to you on a stove, and you ordered him and your own daughter to be put into a barrel and thrown into the sea? I am that same Emelian. And if I feel like it I will burn up and destroy all your kingdom.'

At this threat the tsar was very frightened, and he pleaded for forgiveness.

'My dear Emelian,' he said, 'marry my daughter, take my kingdom, only do not kill me.'

'Oh, all right,' said Emelian.

And they gave a banquet for all the world to enjoy. After which Emelian married Princess Maria and became ruler of the kingdom in place of the tsar.

The Magic Ring

IN DAYS LONG AGO, in a certain village lived a widow whose sole support was her son, Simon. Though he was old enough to marry, he had not found any girl he loved. They were farmers, but they lived in great poverty; they slept on straw, wore only old clothes which they were always patching, and had little to eat. In those days the peasants did not own much land, and the land they did possess was not fertile. If the peasants sowed crops in the autumn they were often frozen during the hard winter; if they came through the frosts they were withered by drought in the summer, or spoilt by heavy rains. And if the sun and the rain spared the crops, the locusts ate them.

As a widow's son, every month Simon had to go to the town to draw a pension: it amounted to a farthing a month. One day he was walking back home with his farthing when he saw a man put a rope round a dog's neck and start to strangle it. The dog was quite a small, white puppy.

'Why are you torturing the puppy?' Simon asked the man.

'What is that to do with you?' the man answered. 'If I choose to kill it, it is none of your business.'

'Then sell it to me for a farthing,' Simon proposed.

'Done! It is yours.'

Simon handed over his farthing, picked up the puppy and went home, thinking:

'I have no cow, I have no horse, but I have a puppy.'

But when he carried the puppy into their hut his mother was angry.

'You are a stupid sort of son to me,' she reproached him. 'We ourselves have nothing to eat, and you go and buy a dog.'

'Do not worry, mother,' Simon answered. 'A puppy is cattle too. It does not low, but it barks.'

A month later Simon went to the town again to draw the pension. And this time he was entitled to an extra pension, so he was given two farthings. As he was returning home he saw the same man tormenting a cat. Simon ran up to him and asked:

'Why are you torturing a living creature?'

'What is it to do with you?' the man demanded. 'It is my cat, isn't it?'

'Then sell her to me.'

'You can have it then. Only, you know a cat is dearer than a dog.'

And he agreed to sell the cat for two farthings.

When Simon carried the cat home his mother was even angrier than before. She grumbled at him all the rest of the day, and started again next morning.

The following month Simon went as usual to draw the pension, and this time was given another farthing. So he set off on his way back with three farthings in his pocket. But on the way he saw the very same man about to crush a snake on the road. And he said to him:

'Do not kill it. Look what a fine snake it is! I have never seen one like it before. And I do not suppose it is poisonous. Why not sell it to me?'

So he bought the snake for three farthings, all the money he had, put it in his breast pocket, and went home. In his pocket the snake was warmed, and it began to talk to him, saying:

'Do not regret giving your three farthings for me, Simon,' it said. 'I am not an ordinary snake, I am the daughter of the Tsar Serpent. If you had not bought me the man would have killed me; but as you have saved me my father will reward you.'

When Simon reached home he took the snake out of his pocket. The moment she saw it his mother climbed on top of the stove and could not even get her breath to scold him: she was speechless with fear. But the snake crawled under the stove, curled itself up and went to sleep.

So they all began to live together: the white dog and the grey cat, the snake, and

Simon and his mother: five of them. But Simon's mother could not take to the snake; she would not give it anything to eat or drink, and was always treading on its tail. So at last the snake said to Simon:

'Your mother is always making my life a misery. Take me home to my father.'

So it was agreed. The snake started crawling along the road, and Simon followed it. They went on for a long time, both

day and night, until they came to a dense forest. Now Simon wondered where he was going and how he was ever going to get back. But the snake reassured him:

'Do not be afraid, we shall soon be there. This is where the serpent kingdom begins. I am the serpent king's daughter, and before long we shall see my father. But now listen! When I tell him how you saved my life he will thank you and offer you a lot of gold. But do not take it: ask only for the gold ring which he wears on his finger. It is a magic ring. My father is keeping it for me, but I want you to have it.'

When Simon and the serpent princess arrived at the home of the Tsar Serpent the tsar was delighted to see his daughter again. And he said to Simon:

'Thank you for saving my daughter. I would have married her to you without regret, only she is already betrothed. But you can take away as much gold as you wish.'

'I do not want any gold,' Simon answered, 'but give me the ring on your finger. I shall keep it in memory of your daughter. I see that it has a snake's head carved on it, and in the head two green stones shine like eyes.'

The tsar was lost in thought for a time.

But then he took the ring from his finger and gave it to Simon, whispering into his ear the instructions for using the ring in order to call up magical powers.

Then Simon said goodbye to the Tsar Serpent and his daughter, and, as the tsar's adopted son, Aspid, was standing there, he said goodbye to him too. And he went back home to his mother. But that night, when his mother had gone to bed, he shifted the magic ring from one hand to the other, and at once twelve young men appeared before him.

'Greetings, our new master,' they said. 'What do you wish?'

'Brothers,' Simon answered, 'fill my granary with wheat, sugar, and a little butter.'

'It shall be done,' the young men said. And they vanished.

When Simon woke up next morning he saw his mother dipping dry crusts in water and chewing them with her old broken teeth. So he said to her:

'Mother, why do you not make a dough and knead it? Then you could bake pastries with it.'

'Wake up, my son, you are dreaming!' she answered. 'This is the second year we have not had so much as a handful of flour.'

'You go to the granary, Mother, and you will find some.'

'Why, even the mice have all died of starvation in our granary,' she answered. 'What is the point of looking in an empty barn? But I will go along and padlock the door.'

She went to the barn, put out her hand to close the door firmly, and it flew wide open. She fell head first into the flour.

From then on they had a much more comfortable life. Simon sold half the flour, and bought beef with the money. And the cat and dog ate meat every day; good food made their fur glisten.

One night while Simon was asleep he had a dream. As soon as he dozed off he saw a beautiful maiden as clearly as if she were actually there; but when he woke up she vanished. He began to feel a great longing for the girl, but he had no idea where to look for her. So he shifted the serpent's ring from finger to finger. And the twelve young men appeared.

'What are your orders, Master?' they asked.

Simon told them he had seen a beautiful maiden in his sleep, but he did not know where to find her. But wherever she was, that was where he wanted to go. In a flash he found himself in another kingdom, where the beautiful maiden was living. He stopped a local man and asked him where he could find this beautiful maiden.

'But which one?' the man asked.

So Simon told him what she looked like.

'Then she is the tsar's daughter,' the man answered.

Simon shifted the ring, and ordered the young men to carry him to the palace, so that he could see the princess. At once he found himself inside the palace, and he saw the maiden. She was even more beautiful than his dream had represented her. Simon only sighed: now what was he to do? He changed the ring from finger to finger, called up the young men, and told them to take him home.

Now he went on living at home; but he

felt very sad because he could not see the princess. He stopped eating and drinking. His mother noticed how miserable he was, and she asked:

'Are you ill, son, or are you in love?'

'I have fallen in love, Mother,' he said, and told her all about the princess.

But when his mother heard his story she was alarmed, and exclaimed:

'What are you thinking of? Is it possible for a peasant's son to love a princess? The tsars are false and cunning people, they will only laugh at you and call you names, and even rob you of your life. They will never give their daughter in marriage to you or any other peasant. Marry some poor village girl, and you will be happy.'

Simon only said:

'Go, Mother, and arrange for the princess to be betrothed to me.'

But his mother would not go. So Simon wondered what he could do. At last he had an idea. He changed his serpent ring and

called up the young men. They appeared at once and asked:

'What do you wish, Master?'

'I need a mansion,' Simon said, 'and I want it to be ready by tomorrow. And arrange fine rooms in the mansion for my mother, and give her a swansdown bed to sleep in.'

'We shall arrange the mansion,' the young men answered, 'and we shall provide the swansdown bed.'

Next morning, when his mother woke up, at first she could not get out of the bed, for she was half buried in the middle of the swansdown bedding. She gazed round the room and could not recognise it; she rubbed her eyes: was she dreaming?

Then Simon came into her room, and said:

'Good morning, Mother.'

So it must be real! She asked him:

'Where has all this wealth come from?'

'All these goods have come from doing good, mother,' Simon said. 'Now you, too, will have an easier life. And you will be able to betroth me to whom we like; now I am equal to anyone.'

'My word, what a bold, daring son I have,' his mother thought. But he mentioned again what he wanted her to do:

'Go to the tsar and tsaritsa, Mother, and have the princess betrothed to me.'

As his mother went from room to room of the mansion, taking in all its splendour, she thought:

'It is a miracle that has been worked for us. I really will go to the tsar to ask for his daughter,' she resolved. 'Though we are still not his equal, we are not much below him now.'

And she went.

She came to the tsar's palace and entered the dining hall. At that moment the tsar and tsaritsa were drinking tea; as it was hot they had poured the tea into the saucers and were blowing on it. The young princess was looking through her trousseau, which she kept in a chest. The tsar and tsaritsa went on blowing on their saucers and did not even look up when Simon's mother entered. They blew drops of tea out of the saucers and it sprinkled over the table-cloth. Simon's mother could not help thinking: 'Why, the tsar does not even know how to drink tea!' And she scolded them:

'Tea is not water. Why are you spilling it?'

The tsar glanced at her and asked:

'And what do you want?'

She walked into the middle of the hall. 'Good morning, Tsar and emperor,' she said. 'You have goods to sell; we have a merchant who will buy. Would you give your daughter in marriage to our son?'

'But who is this proposed husband?' the tsar asked. 'What is his lineage, who is his father, and from which city does he come?'

'He is a peasant by birth,' Simon's mother replied. 'His father's name was Gregory, and he comes from a village in other parts. Have you never heard of him?'

At that the tsaritsa simply gasped:

'Why, have you taken leave of your

senses?' she exclaimed. 'We are overrun with suitors already, we can choose whom we like. Do you think our daughter would marry a peasant?'

At this answer Simon's mother took offence:

'What kind of peasant do you think he is, Mother?' she retorted. 'He is different: even tsars' sons are as nothing compared with him. And as for girls and daughters, he is good enough to marry the best of them. That is the sort of son I have!'

Now the tsar had a crafty idea. 'Let your son build a crystal bridge from our palace to your front door,' he said. 'Then we will drive over this bridge to have a look at the future husband's home.'

Simon's mother returned to her mansion to tell her son the answer. At the door she ran into the dog and the cat, both looking as smooth as silk. She drove them off furiously. 'You get out!' she scolded them. 'You do nothing but eat and sleep. What good are you?'

'I wasted my time going,' she told her son. 'They would not agree.'

'Are you sure?' Simon asked in astonishment. 'Did they really refuse me?'

'Did you think they would be delighted?'

she answered. 'The tsar even poked fun at us. He said: "Let your son build a crystal bridge from our palace to your house, and we will drive over the crystal bridge to call on you"!'

'That is nothing to us, Mother,' he told her.

That night he moved the ring from one hand to the other, called up the young men, and ordered them to build a crystal bridge by the following morning. It was to run from his front door to the tsar's palace, across all the rivers and ravines. And a self-propelled machine was to be provided to travel over the bridge.

From midnight till dawn, all through the district hammers were knocking and saws sawing. And in the morning when Simon went to his front door he saw the crystal bridge standing ready, and a self-propelled machine was travelling along it. So he said to his mother:

'Now go to the tsar again, Mother. Let them get ready to call on us, and I will drive over in the self-propelled machine to fetch them.'

So his mother set off over the bridge to go to the tsar. But when she set foot on the bridge she found that the crystal was very smooth and slippery. She was so alarmed that she sat down, and, as the wind was blowing at her back, she started to slide, and went sliding all the way to the tsar's palace.

She went straight to the tsar and said:

'Yesterday, when I called on you, you ordered the future husband of your daughter to build a bridge. Look out of the window and you will see the bridge all ready.'

The tsar looked out of the window and exclaimed in surprise:

'You are quite right, there is a bridge. So your son can do things!'

He dressed himself in gold brocade trousers, put the crown on his head, called the tsaritsa, and went to the door. He stepped on to the bridge and shook the balustrade to make sure it was safe. He smacked his hands against the crystal bricks, just in case they were not real. But the bridge was quite well built.

At that moment Simon drove up in his marvellous self-propelled machine. He opened its door and said:

'Get in, my lord the tsar and your consort wife, and drive to be our guests.'

'I shall be very willing,' the tsar said, 'but my wife might be a little afraid.'

Simon went to speak to the tsaritsa, to reassure her, but she waved him away:

'I am not going to ride in that thing,' she told him. 'It is fearful. It might overturn into the river, and that would be a fine how-do-you-do!'

The tsar's courtiers came up and talked to the tsar. His chamberlain advised him:

'It would be advisable to ride in it, my lord the tsar, just to set an example. Do not let them think you are frightened.'

There was no other way out, so the tsar

and tsaritsa got into the machine, while the courtiers clung on to the back, to the axles, or hung on the handles. The machine whistled, roared, howled, shuddered, rang the bell, puffed out steam and heat, leaped forward and set off. As they rode they swayed from side to side. Thank goodness they had not far to go! There was only one bridge to cross.

When they arrived at Simon's mansion he got out of the machine, and went to open the door for the tsar. But the courtiers got there first. They dragged the tsar and tsaritsa out of the machine, fanned them with fans, and brought them back to life, for they were half-dead with fright. When she revived the tsaritsa was furious, and the tsar, though he would not say a word, evidently agreed with her.

'Oh, I am feeling sick,' the tsaritsa screamed. 'I have been jolted and shaken to pieces, and look at me: I am all dishevelled. Oh, you devil, where are you, our daughter's future husband? Take the girl when you like, but we are going back home on foot.'

So everything turned out as Simon wished. The tsar gave him his daughter for his wife, and they began to live together At first they were very happy.

But then something happened. Simon and his wife went for a walk in the forest. They walked a long way, grew very tired, and lay down under a tree to have a nap. And Aspid, the Tsar Serpent's adopted son, was wandering through the forest that day. He came to the sleeping pair, saw the tsar's ring on Simon's finger, and in his envy he turned into a viper. He had long wanted to possess that ring, he knew its magic power and had asked the Tsar Serpent to give it to him. But the tsar had refused, and he had never told him how to make use of its magic.

Aspid saw a chance to get hold of the ring now, and he turned himself into a beautiful maiden, one even more beautiful than Simon's young wife. Then he woke up Simon and tried to entice him to leave his wife and come to him. 'And then the ring will be mine,' Aspid thought. But Simon took one look at the beautiful stranger who was trying to allure him, and told her:

'Go back where you came from. Beautiful as you are, even more beautiful than my wife, I am fond of her and shall not go with you.'

And he went to sleep again.

So Aspid turned himself into a handsome young man, finer than one could ever hope

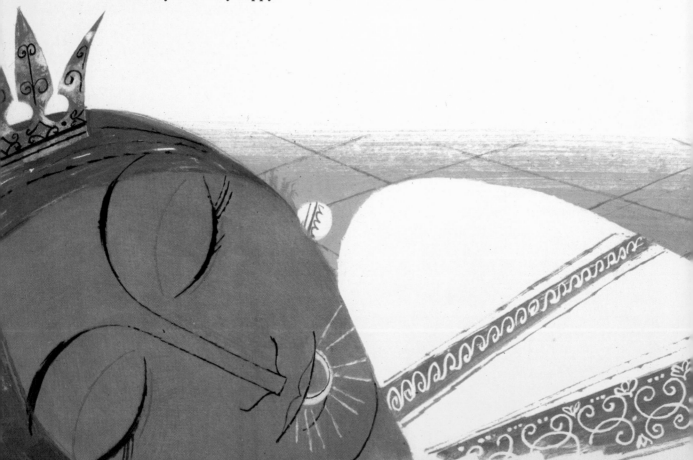

to see. He woke up the princess, Simon's wife, and showed himself off to her.

'Why, he really is handsome,' the princess thought. 'Handsomer than Simon. If only I had had a man like him for suitor before I married this Simon!'

Aspid went up to the princess and held out his hand to her. The princess took his hand and got up. Then she looked at Simon: his face was dirty, his nostrils were blowing dust about. And she turned back to Aspid and asked:

'Who are you?'

'I am a tsar's son, called the Bravest of the Brave.'

'And I am a tsar's daughter,' she said.

'Come with me,' he enticed her. 'I shall do you no harm.'

'Come along, then,' said Simon's wife. And she gave him her hand.

Aspid whispered into her ear what she was to do, and the princess agreed to everything he suggested. Then Aspid left her, after instructing her to find out from Simon how the magic ring worked, and then to get it from Simon and bring it to him.

So she went home with her husband, taking him by the hand and asking whether it was true that he wore a magic ring on his finger. And she said that if he really loved her he would tell her how the ring was used. In his goodness of heart Simon told her how to work the ring, for he thought: 'She loves me, so she may as well know about the ring; she will not do me any harm.' And he put the ring on his wife's finger. After all, whenever he had need of it he could get it back.

But that same night the princess shifted the ring from one finger to another, and at once the twelve young men appeared.

'And how can we serve you, our new mistress?' they asked.

'This is what I want you to do,' she said. 'Take this mansion and the crystal bridge and transfer it to the place where the Bravest of the Brave lives. And put Simon and his mother back in their cottage.'

So Simon, Gregory's son, was not married to his princess for long!

When he and his mother awoke next morning they found they had nothing except their old poor cottage and an empty barn. Simon had only himself and his mother, a cat, and a dog, four of them altogether, with nothing to eat. He did not sigh, he did not complain. He remembered what his mother had said to him: 'Do not

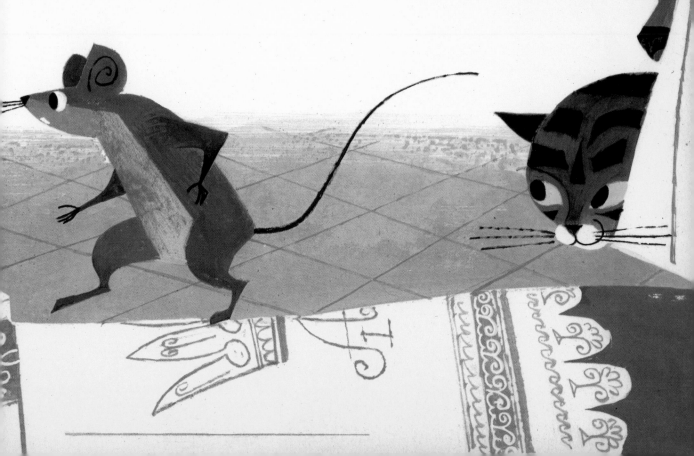

marry a princess. You will not be happy.'
But he had not listened to her.

While he was thinking these sad thoughts
he happened to look out of the window, and
saw a carriage coming along, with the tsar
in it. The tsar stepped out of his carriage
right outside Simon's window, and looked
about him, wondering what had happened:
there was no mansion, no crystal bridge, no
fine display, no brilliance, only a poverty-
stricken cottage, and Simon looking out at
the tsar through the cottage window.

The tsar was thoroughly annoyed. He
shouted to Simon:

'What is all this? Where is my daughter,
the princess? You are a fraud!'

Simon went out to the tsar and told him
exactly what had happened: how the tsar's
daughter had taken his magic ring and had
tricked him. But the tsar would not believe
his story. He was furious, and gave orders
for Simon to be put in prison until he confessed what he had done with the princess.

Simon was taken away from his mother,

and she was left without anyone to provide for her. And she began to starve. She called the cat and the dog to go with her, and went begging. She stood outside one window and begged for bread, and outside another window she sat down to eat it. But now the days were growing cold and dark, the summer was growing old, winter was coming on.

So the cat said to the dog:

'We shall all be lost. Let us go and find the princess and take the magic ring from her. Our master saved us from death; now we shall save him.'

The dog agreed. He sniffed at the ground and ran off down the road, with the cat after him. They had to run a very long way. That is easy to say, but their journey was not so easy to run. They ran on and on until they saw the crystal bridge and Simon's mansion, in which they too had lived for a time.

The dog remained outside, while the cat went in. She made her way to the bedchamber where the princess, Simon's cheating wife, was sleeping. The cat saw that she was holding the magic ring in her mouth, for it was shining between her teeth. Evidently she was afraid someone might steal it. The cat caught a mouse, bit its ear, and told it to be a sensible mouse and do what she told it. The mouse promised to be good, and climbed on to the bed, silently walked over the princess and began to tickle her nose with its tail. The princess sneezed and took a deep breath: the ring fell on the floor and rolled away. The cat snatched it up and jumped through the window.

When the princess woke she found she had lost the ring. But by the time she started looking for it the mouse which had tickled her nose was already in the kitchen, nibbling a crust as though it had never had anything to do with the ring.

The cat and the dog ran all the way home; they were in such a hurry, they did not stop to eat or drink. They scurried over mountains and through the dense forests, they swam across rivers and tore over the open fields. The cat held the magic ring firmly under her tongue and never opened her

mouth. At last they saw before them the last river they had to cross; and on the other side of the river they could see their village, where Simon's cottage was.

The dog said to the cat:

'Sit on my back, and I will swim across. But be sure to hold the ring firmly in your teeth. Do not drop it.'

He started swimming across the river. When they reached the middle the dog said:

'Do not say a word, Cat, or you will lose the ring in the water.'

The cat said nothing. The dog swam a little farther, and said again:

'Do not speak, Cat.'

But the cat had not opened her mouth for an instant. But the dog simply had to say to her again:

'Do not speak, Cat.'

And yet the cat had not even attempted to speak. Even so, the dog was so anxious that before they reached the shore he said once more:

'Cat, do not speak.'

At that the cat lost all patience. She opened her mouth and protested:

'But I am not speaking, not a word.'

And the ring dropped into the river.

When they climbed out on to the bank they started to scold and reproach each other. The dog yapped:

'It is all your fault; you talk too much.'

But the cat retorted:

'No it is not, it is yours, you yapper. Why did you keep on yapping at me when I had not said a word?'

Just then some fishermen drew fish on to the bank with the nets and began to gut it. They saw the dog and cat snarling at each other, and thought they were hungry. So they threw them the parts of the fish they did not want. The dog and cat were hungry; they snatched up the pieces of fish and set to work to eat them. But they had not got far with their dinner when one of them grated its teeth on something hard. When they looked, they saw it was the magic ring.

They left the rest of the fish uneaten, and ran into the village. They went past their cottage, just to see if their master was at home. But he was not in, and his mother was out begging. So they ran off to the town, to find the prison in which Simon was shut away.

When they came to the prison the cat climbed on to the wall and walked along the top, to see if she could see Simon. She would have liked to miaow or purr, but she had the ring under her tongue, and was afraid of dropping it. Late in the afternoon Simon looked through his cell window, to take a last look at the sunset. The cat saw him, and made her way down a drainpipe and climbed the wall to get into the cell.

Simon was glad to see her, and took her in his arms. 'She is only a cat,' he was thinking, 'but she has a faithful heart. She remembers me.' But the cat miaowed, and dropped the magic ring on the floor. Simon picked it up, shifted it from one finger to another, and called up the twelve young men. They appeared at once.

'Greetings, our good master,' they said. 'Tell us what you want done and we will do it at once.'

'Bring my mansion back to the spot where it was before,' Simon said. 'And anyone who happens to be in it is to be left in the rooms: I should like to see them. And carry the crystal bridge back here, but do not set the farther end down by the tsar's palace; put it in the next village to mine.'

It was all done as he asked. The mansion was restored to its place, and in it he found the young princess with Aspid. Of course they had to leave Simon's mansion, and they went to live with the princess's father, the tsar. They had nowhere else to go. When Aspid found out that she had lost the ring he was so furious that he turned into a viper. And he was never able to change into a handsome young man again, because he always felt spiteful towards the princess. So he remained a viper for the rest of his life, doing nothing all day but hiss at the princess and quarrel with her.

And then the tsar, her father, remembered Simon, and said:

'Ah, that Simon fellow may have been one of the people, but he was a good little chap. And this Aspid may be of royal lineage, but he is a viper all the same.'

Simon and his mother went back to their mansion, taking the dog and the cat with them. Simon goes visiting the next village on his self-propelled machine every day. It is quite a short journey over the crystal bridge. I have heard, too, that Simon intends to marry an orphan girl in that village. She is said to be even more beautiful than the princess, and he has been betrothed to her. So I expect Simon will marry the orphan girl, have lots of children, and a new fairy tale will have its beginning.